SHOWING SHEEP

SELECT, FEED, FIT, & SHOW

By Laura Lawson

LDF Publications
Culpeper, Virginia

SHOWING SHEEP

SELECT, FEED, FIT, & SHOW

By Laura Lawson

Published by:
LDF Publications
11114 Lawson Lane, Culpeper, VA 22701
PROBLEM? If you have purchased this book, and have a problem, contact us by email from our website-www.sheepbooks.com
Orderline: toll-free 1-800-258-6992

This publication is designed to provide accurate and authoritative information in regard to the subject covered. It is sold with the understanding that the author and publisher are not rendering veterinary, nutritional or other professional service. If expert assistance is required, the service of a competent professional person should be sought.

First printing August, 1994
Second printing May, 1995
Third printing April, 1996
Forth printing July, 1999
Fifth printing March, 2002

Library of Congress Catalog Card Number 94-78838

ISBN: 0-9633923-2-8

CONTENTS

PREPARING FOR A SHOW PROJECT

THE HOME COMING

CARE AND FEEDING FOR SHOW

SIXTY DAYS BEFORE THE SHOW

TRAINING FOR THE SHOWRING

THIRTY DAYS BEFORE THE SHOW

FITTING SHEEP FOR SHOWING

TRAVELING AND CARE AT THE SHOW

DEDICATION

This book is dedicated to all 4-H and FFA sheep club leaders, and especially to Mason Hutcheson, Extension Agent in Culpeper, VA, now retired.

These leaders throughout the country unselfishly spend untold voluntary hours working with our youth.

Mason, like all of the leaders I have met, has spent countless evenings and weekends planning all sorts of activities from educational meetings to county shows and fairs.

Mason has given, and continues to give, our young people family values and community spirit. He always encourages the whole family to become involved with the sheep club. Older brothers and sisters often help the adults with the activities, while younger brothers and sisters learn about sheep even before they are old enough to officially be in a club.

Because of this dedication to our young people, I am proud to be able to dedicate this book to Mason and to all sheep club leaders everywhere.

ACKNOWLEDGMENTS

I want to thank all those who provided me with information and pictures. This book would not have been possible without their help.

I would especially like to thank Dr. John Glenn, University of California at Davis and the staff of the University's Visual Media Department, who furnished many of the pictures found in this book.

For those who may not know, The Visual Media Department has an extensive library of audio, slide, and video presentations available for rent and purchase.

Subjects covered include raising and showing all types of livestock, food and nutrition, plants of all kinds, and many more. These presentations are great for 4-H and FFA programs. Call them at (916) 757-8980.

Additional materials were provided by:

Jane Hobbs, sheep producer and former publisher of Sheep Producer Magazine, Arlington, KY.

John C. P. Kroge, "Of Sheep & Shows", Paddock Publishing, Bolder, CO.

M. E. Ensminger and R. O. Parker, :Sheep & Goat Science", The Interstate Printers & Publishers, Danville, IL.

TO THE PARENTS

Dear Parent:

If you are reading this, it is because you are considering or have decided to encourage your child to participate in a sheep showing project.

This is not just another book about teaching children how to capture blue ribbons. Only a few will win a blue ribbon, and some of them will miss the true prize - development of life's worthwhile values.

This book was written mainly to teach children how to choose and care for show sheep. As a teaching tool, showing sheep can help develop self-confidence, principles, and standards that are needed to become worthwhile adults.

We sometimes place too much emphasis on winning first place and miss a golden opportunity to reinforce worthwhile values. Another definition of winning is "achievement". Even the beginner or last-placed child in the show ring is a winner when winning is defined as achievement.

Winning is about success in advancing from a beginning point. Parents should encourage achievement by putting more emphasis on the positive benefits of showing sheep and less on winning a blue ribbon.

Keep in mind that before a child can run it must first learn to sit up, then crawl, and finally walk. A beginner who knows nothing about raising and showing sheep could easily be considered a winner even if the animal placed last, simply because he/she put forth an effort.

Occasionally we forget that the purpose behind youth shows is to afford children the opportunity to learn more than just winning a blue ribbon. If emphasis is placed on some of the other rewards of showing, it can be a vehicle for stressing a child's self worth and becomes a means of molding the child into a worthwhile adult.

Showing sheep usually turns into a family activity. It is a very rewarding experience for your child and the family if it is approached correctly. It can offer an opportunity to pass on character-building values to your child.

Children learn to work with other people toward a common goal and become more self-assured, responsible, independent, confident, and courteous. They are more at ease around strangers and adults.

Your child will expand his or her knowledge of livestock by meeting and working with all age groups of people involved in the sheep industry. A sheep project should be considered a fun and fellowship opportunity for your child. Financial remuneration should not be the main goal of the parent or the child, anymore than sending a child to camp would result in financial gain.

Providing our children with good, sound animals is essential. We shouldn't purchase sheep based strictly on price.

Children who are provided with expensive animals sometimes assume that this guarantees them a blue ribbon. They need to understand their obligation and the part they must play in creating a winner.

If your child is a beginner in caring for and showing sheep, it isn't necessary to purchase the best, most expensive animal around. Beginners lack the knowledge to properly feed, groom, and show their sheep. This will come with experience. More expensive animals can be selected in the future as the child's skills develop.

However, a beginner's animal should be good enough in quality to compete. We need to encourage the child to gain experience, learn sportsmanship and to continue year after year.

Children who place higher in a class each year are encouraged to try harder to improve their skills. It gives them a goal to strive for.

INTRODUCTION

Showing sheep can be great fun. It can be a rewarding adventure for you and your family. You will get a chance to make new friends, go to places where sheep are raised or sold, and learn more about sheep and the people who raise and sell them.

Sheep shows can be as exciting as any sporting event. You will need to learn many things if you want to be a part of this exciting activity. Your adventure will begin by learning how to pick out an animal that has a chance of winning a ribbon at one of your local shows.

After you have selected your animal, you will need to learn how to feed and care for it. You will also need to know how to train it for the show ring and how to prepare it for a show. Many hours of practice will be needed to develop these skills.

It is important to remember that a sheep project isn't as much about winning as it is about sharing, helping, and having fun. Even if you don't win a ribbon, you will have fun and learn a lot that will help you the next time you show.

Picking out your sheep is only the beginning. It will be several months before you and your sheep are ready to go to a show. Both you and your sheep will need to learn a lot and work hard to be ready for the show. You will spend many hours together learning about each other, playing and working together and becoming friends.

Before you decide to show, you should ask yourself the following question. "Am I willing to make a commitment?" This simply means to make a promise to take good care of the animal and learn as much as you can about it.

Sometimes kids want their family to feed, water, groom and take care of the sheep for them. If you take on this project, it should be with the knowledge that the sheep will depend on you for everything.

JOHN AND JAY AND THEIR SHEEP

I once knew twin brothers, John and Jay, who were 11 years old. They begged their parents to buy them each a lamb to show at their local county fair. They looked at lambs at many farms.

"We are going home with John and Jay!"

Finally, they found twin wether lambs at a farm that they thought were the best of all. The farmer told them, "I think one of these lambs is a little better than the other but either could be a champion if fed and taken care of properly."

The boys were very excited. They bought the lambs and drew straws to see who would get the lamb the farmer thought was the better of the two. John won the draw.

The farmer gave each lamb an injection of Vitamin B before they were loaded onto the truck. He told the boys that Vitamin B helps keep the lambs from getting sick from stress.

Lambs sometimes are stressed when they have to travel a long distance or are moved to a new home. They miss their mother and friends. The boys had just received their first lesson in taking care of lambs.

The next lesson the boys learned was about feeding. The farmer gave the boys some of the feed the lambs were used to eating. He told them to mix it with some of the feed they planned to use for their lambs. This would keep the lambs from getting an upset stomach.

The farmer did everything he could to be sure that the boys arrived home with two healthy lambs. He told the boys the rest was up to them.

The boys were very excited by the time they arrived home. That night, as they lie in their beds, they made plans about how they were going to feed and take care of their lambs. Later, John had dreams of winning a blue ribbon but Jay had dreams of having fun with his new lamb.

Both boys fed and took good care of their lambs. The lambs soon began to recognize them and would bleat as soon as they saw them. The lambs became very tame and followed the boys everywhere. They constantly nudged them; wanting the boys to pet or play with them.

The boys agreed that John's lamb would surely win a ribbon at the show even if it wasn't a blue ribbon. Both lambs were gaining weight quickly but there was just something special about John's lamb that made him stand out. It was that little something extra that says, "Look at me, I'm special, I'm a champion."

After a few weeks, John began spending less and less time with his lamb. He was tired of feeding and playing with the lamb. He wanted to go hang out with his friends or watch TV and made excuses whenever he forgot to feed his lamb.

After a while John's lamb acted as if he didn't really know him. The lamb would run away from him whenever he came into the pen. John stayed away from the lamb more and more until the lamb was no longer tame.

Jay did things different from John. Jay fed and watered his lamb morning and night. He ran and played with him. They played in the sprinkler together. Jay even taught his lamb to jump into a tub of water for a bath. On really hot days, Jay would jump in with him. They had great fun together.

Jay taught his lamb the things he would need to know in the show ring. Jay put a halter on him and taught him how to walk alongside him. He taught him how to place his feet and stand perfectly still.

Each time Jay's lamb learned something new or did a good job, Jay rewarded him with a small piece of apple or a couple of peanuts. The lamb soon learned that his treat was in Jay's pocket. If Jay put the treat in another pocket, the lamb would sniff around until he discovered it. Jay and his lamb became good friends.

Jay felt sorry for John's lamb. Sometimes Jay would take pity on John's lamb because he looked so sad. He would try to give him a piece of apple or some peanuts but the lamb would run away.

The week of the show finally came. The lambs were weighed and Jay's lamb weighed 20 pounds more than John's lamb. The boys' parents asked how this could be. John made excuses and said, "My lamb isn't as good as Jay's." His parents reminded him of what the farmer had said about the lamb but John just made more excuses.

Jay had some free time after his lamb was weighed and his lamb was ready for the show so he walked around the fair, visited some exhibits, and made some new friends. John and his lamb were not ready. John spent all of his time practicing setting his lamb's feet and trying to train him to a halter.

On the day of the show, Jay and his lamb were ready to show but John wasn't. John's lamb was still very scared and didn't want anyone touching him. When the boys led their lambs into the show ring, Jay's lamb pranced along proudly by his side. John's lamb fought the halter and jumped up into the air.

John became very upset with his lamb. Every time John tried to walk with his lamb, the lamb would lie down on the ground. Finally after a lot of work, John got his lamb into the ring. He was one of the last ones to come into the ring so he was near the end of the line.

John was so embarrassed that all he could think of was wishing that the show was over and that he could stay right where he was so that he wouldn't have to move his lamb.

The judge looked closely at each lamb and made some decisions. He started moving lambs around. John gritted his teeth but the judge didn't ask him to move.

Finally, the judge placed Jay and his lamb first. John and his lamb were next to last.

Jay held his breath and hoped his excitement wouldn't make his lamb nervous. Finally, the judge walked up and slapped Jay's lamb on the rump and said, "This is my Champion."

The judge shook Jay's hand and congratulated him. After thanking the judge, Jay put his arms around his lamb's neck and gave him a big hug. He whispered to him, "We did it boy, can you believe it, we did it!"

John was angry and jealous of his brother. "That really was the lamb I wanted but my brother got him." John said to Linda, who was standing in line next to him. "He won because he got the better lamb."

The judge made comments about all the lambs that were being shown. When the judge got to John and his lamb, he said, "This boy has one of the best lambs in the show as far as conformation goes. If it had been worked and fed a little more it would have been hard to deny it the championship honors."

John got tears in his eyes. Now he knew it wasn't his lamb that cost him the blue ribbon. John realized that it takes more than a good lamb to have a Champion; it takes dedication and commitment. John decided right then and there that next year he was going to do a better job.

After the boys got their lambs back to the pens, John congratulated Jay for winning. He grinned at him and said, "Just wait till next year, I'm going to do a better job than I did this year and I may just beat you."

26

John was true to his word. The following year John worked very hard. He and his lamb practiced every day. He made sure his lamb was fed and watered each day on time.

John told his mother "My lamb is sure a little pig. I have to keep giving him more and more to eat. He wants to eat all the time. I have to exercise him to keep him from getting too fat."

John's lamb gained more and more. John's parents were even afraid that the lamb might get too heavy before show day. He didn't. He was just right.

John's lamb was named the Champion of the show. Jay's lamb came in second. Jay laughingly told John the same thing that John had said to him the year before, "Just wait till next year."

This story reminds us that winning is a partnership between the exhibitor and the lamb. The best lamb in the country can't become a champion without the dedication and commitment of the boy or girl that is caring for it.

Showing sheep is about more that just winning. It is also about having fun, making friends, and practicing good sportsmanship.

PREPARING FOR A SHOW PROJECT

Your sheep may be purchased or you may raise them from birth. Either way, there are some things you should know and do before you start your project.

GROUP RAISING

Show sheep should be raised as a group of 2 or more even if only one is actually shown.

Sheep are raised in pairs because they keep each other company. This results in better health, less stress, and better appetites. Two or more sheep eating together will each eat more and gain more weight.

All sheep in the group should be similar in type and weight so that they can receive the same feed and training.

CHOOSING A BREED

What breed should you choose? This will depend on your goals.

If you plan to enter your sheep in a breeding class, you will need to contact the breed associations of the breeds you are considering. Ask them for as much information as possible about their breed. Then you can choose the breed that is right for you.

If your goal is to win a market lamb class, then you may want to select a lamb from a meat breed or a cross of two meat breeds.

VIRGINIA FAIR CHAMPION SUFFOLK EWE

The largest of the meat breeds are the Suffolk and Hampshire breeds. Dorsets are considered medium-framed. These breeds and their crosses are the most popular lambs found at market shows. Other breeds and crosses have won shows but most judges seem to make the meat breeds and their crosses the champions.

Finally, it may be your own likes and dislikes that help you decide which breed or cross you would like to show. The main thing to remember is to use only good sheep that have a chance of winning their class.

HOUSING AND EQUIPMENT

Before you select and bring your sheep home, you need to decide where you are going to keep them. You also need to collect a few pieces of basic equipment.

SHELTER

You should provide housing large enough to hold them. Each animal needs a minimum of 10 square feet. A larger space should be used if possible.

Large sheep and those being raised in hot or humid climates should be given more space. A larger shelter stays drier and there are fewer bacteria and fly problems.

Your shelter should protect your sheep from the sun and rain. The shelter can be a simple structure consisting of a roof and one, two or three open sides. This type shelter helps provide enough air movement during hot weather.

Keeping sheep cool is very important during hot weather. When no breeze is blowing, you may need to hang a fan in the shelter. Sheep will stop eating and not gain weight if they are too hot. They can become sick from the heat. This condition is called heat stress.

If you live in the North, you may want to use a shelter or shed that is enclosed on three sides. This type shelter will give your sheep more protection from cold driving rain and wind.

BEDDING
You need to put bedding down on the floor of your shelter. The kind of bedding used will depend on the area where you live. Many people use good clean straw, sand, or wood shavings.

A thick layer of bedding, no matter what bedding you use, will help keep the area drier. The sheep cover up their manure when they walk back and forth and urine soaks through leaving the bedding dry.

EXERCISE AREA
The shelter should be part of a fenced exercise area. Exercise is important. Sheep need plenty of exercise just as we do.

The exercise area should be large so that the sheep can run around without running into each other or their feeders and waterers.

The fencing used to build the exercise area should be safe for the sheep. Loose boards, wires, and nails can hurt them. Make the fence strong. You want the sheep to stay in and dogs to stay out.

WATER CONTAINER
You can use many different kinds of containers to supply water for the sheep.

A 5 gallon bucket or small 10 to 12 gallon tub set upon cement blocks can be used for two or three animals. You do not want the sheep to kick dirt into the water. The water container should be emptied, cleaned, and refilled with fresh water at least twice each day. Each animal can drink a gallon of fresh water on a hot day.

Pick a container that can be emptied and cleaned easily. Sheep will not drink dirty or hot water. If the sheep do not drink water, they will eat less. This often is the cause of weight loss in market lambs.

FEED CONTAINER

HANGING FEED CONTAINER

Feeders can be as simple as a wood trough. Feeders should be built up off the ground because sheep like to paw the ground while they eat. Sheep kick dirt and manure into feeders if the feeders are on the ground.

Molded plastic or fiberglass feeders can be purchased from supply stores. These feeders easily hang on a panel, gate or board fence. They are inexpensive and very easy to keep clean.

Hanging feeders have other advantages. You can increase the size of the sheep's back leg muscles by hanging the feeder high and placing a step on the ground under the feeder. Each time the sheep step up to eat, they exercise their back leg muscles. This is important if you have a lamb that is going to be shown in a market class.

Hanging feeders are also lightweight, portable, and ideal for feeding the sheep later on at fairs and shows.

SELECTION
Before you select your show sheep, you need to know what sound animals look like.

This section of the book covers health, body type, and conformation. Where to buy sheep and how much to pay for them is covered for those planning to buy their sheep.

HEALTH
Health is important to growth.

34

Sick, weak, or thin sheep will continue to have health problems. They will not gain weight as they should.

Healthy, strong animals are lively and active. They eat more and gain weight faster than sick animals.

Try to select your animals after they have been shorn. Health problems can be hidden by the wool.

Look for alert, clear eyes. There should be a nice pink color to the inside of the eyelids. There should be fine pink veins showing in the white portion of the eyeball. Sheep with pale or white eyelids and eyeballs usually have internal parasites (worms).

Avoid animals with damp fleece under their eyes or ones with an eye discharge or irritated bright red eyelids. They may have an eye infection or a cold.

Don't select animals that are coughing. Coughing is a sign of pneumonia or scar tissue left over from a previous bout with pneumonia. These animals are easily stressed.

Look to see if the sheep's back end is dirty from diarrhea. Diarrhea means the lamb may have an infection or internal worms.

Select animals that have been dewormed and vaccinated against the main diseases that affect show animals. These diseases are overeating, pneumonia, and soremouth.

The animal needs a minimum of two overeating and pneumonia vaccinations and a single vaccination for soremouth.

Check the feet and between the toes of each animal. If you smell a bad odor, you should clean or trim the hooves to make sure the animal doesn't have foot rot. You will not be able to show an animal with foot rot.

Lambs should be 60 days of age or older. Select only lambs that have been docked, castrated, and weaned for at least two weeks. These procedures cause stress that affects the lamb's immune system and lowers its resistance to disease. The added stress of moving the lamb could be enough to make the lamb sick.

Lambs should be eating large amounts of grain or feed pellets. They should be full-fledged ruminants before they are removed from their mother. This means that they should be bringing up a cud and chewing it.

TYPE
Type refers to a combination of characteristics which make sheep useful for production. Type in breeding animals can be divided into meat or wool type. Market lambs should have traits that are common to meat type breeds.

Type is also used to describe predominant traits for each breed of purebred sheep. The selection of purebred breeding animals should fit the characteristics for the particular breed type.

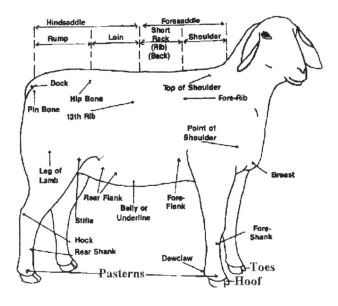

BODY PARTS

Type sometimes is used interchangeably with conformation because it does involve the conformation of an animal. An animal's conformation refers to its structure, outline, or general shape. Selection for proper conformation is the first step to having a successful show animal.

A sheep's body parts should be as close as possible to what is considered ideal or perfect. The different body parts are identified in the above Illustration.

CONFORMATION -- BALANCE

It is important to know what makes up ideal conformation for a market lamb or a breeding animal before you can judge the conformation of each particular animal.

Desirable conformation should include a long strong level back with a rump that is long and level with good large legs underneath it.

The most useful animal will have deep flanks, good length and depth of loin, and legs that show natural muscling. There should be substantial width between the rear legs with the proper amount of strength and balance.

When judges speak of balance, they usually are referring to the correctness of the animal's structure. They are indicating whether the sheep's body parts are desirably proportioned and blended together smoothly.

STRUCTURAL FAULTS

A sound mouth, eyes, feet, and legs are basic to good health and performance in all sheep. These points should be checked upon before considering any animal whether it be for a market or breeding class.

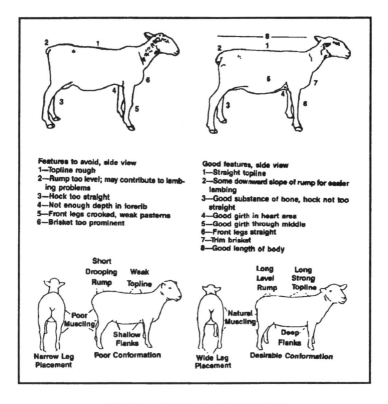

Features to avoid, side view
1—Topline rough
2—Rump too level; may contribute to lambing problems
3—Hock too straight
4—Not enough depth in forerib
5—Front legs crooked, weak pasterns
6—Brisket too prominent

Good features, side view
1—Straight topline
2—Some downward slope of rump for easier lambing
3—Good substance of bone, hock not too straight
4—Good girth in heart area
5—Good girth through middle
6—Front legs straight
7—Trim brisket
8—Good length of body

Short Drooping Rump   Weak Topline
Poor Muscling
Shallow Flanks
Narrow Leg Placement   Poor Conformation

Long Level Rump   Long Strong Topline
Natural Muscling
Deep Flanks
Wide Leg Placement   Desirable Conformation

GOOD AND POOR FEATURES

If you are a beginner, it may be necessary for you to have someone more experienced help you check these points when you select your sheep. See the *Illustration -- GOOD AND POOR FEATURES*.

Sheep that lack sound mouths, eyes, feet or legs will not grow properly. Structural problems that can be seen clearly in lambs at a young age become worse as the lamb gets older.

MOUTH

A sheep's teeth must meet its dental pad evenly. This means that they should not be in front of nor behind the pad.

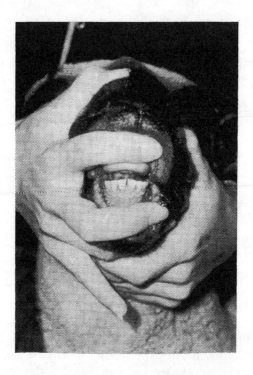

If the teeth are in front of the pad, the sheep's lower jaw is too long. This is called a bull-dog mouth. If the teeth are located behind the dental pad, the sheep's lower jaw is too short. This is known as being parrot mouthed. Both of these conditions are inherited defects.

Lambs born with lower jaws either longer or shorter than their upper jaws should not be selected as show lambs. If a lamb's teeth do not correctly meet the pad, it will be unable to eat properly. Therefore it will not gain at as rapid a rate as one with a sound mouth.

Occasionally, older lambs who have been fed nothing but a heavy show feed have their teeth slightly forward of the pad. The gums have become soft from lack of exercise. This condition can usually be corrected by allowing the lamb to graze pasture or by adding something to the feed for the lamb to chew upon, such as corn cobs.

Judges usually check the teeth of all sheep being shown. If a sheep's teeth don't meet its pad, it is considered a fault. Sheep with unsound mouths normally place lower in their class.

EYES
Always check the eyes of the sheep you are considering for show.

If the sheep's lower eyelids roll out (hang open), it may have a condition called ectropion. Dust can collect in the open eyelids and can cause an irritation.

Lambs born with eyelids that turn in toward the eyeball have a condition called entropion. The lashes of the eyelid make the eyeball irritated (sore and red). This may cause the eye to water leaving damp wool under the eye. If the condition is severe enough, it can cause blindness.

41

Do not select an animal with either of these problems.

FEET AND LEGS
Sound feet and legs are very important.

Animals with sound feet and legs stand up well on the front of their toes and have medium length pasterns. The pastern is that part of the foot between the dew claw and the hoof.

Long pasterns can make the animal's foot sore and can cause breeding problems when they are older. Animals with long pasterns are seen more often in the larger breeds of sheep.

Fast growing lambs with long pasterns often go down on their pasterns. The bones are not thick enough to support the extra weight. Sometimes the animal walks with its heels touching the ground.

Sheep with sore feet stand less. Therefore, they do not eat nor gain weight well. Weak pasterns affect the muscle development. If an animal goes down too far on its pasterns, it will be placed lower in a class by most judges.

Long, weak pasterns cause problems in animals intended for breeding. Rams with sore feet spend less time breeding. Ewes with sore feet may not spend enough time eating nor getting enough exercise to produce healthy lambs.

42

The legs should have thick bones and be straight. The feet should be spaced apart in the front and in the back.

SOUND STRUCTURE AND CONFORMATION

HEAD AND NECK
A good head and neck give sheep "eye appeal". Although the head and neck are not the most important part of the animal, they can be the only thing that sets apart sheep of equal conformation. This may be the little extra that makes an animal stand out and get the judge's attention and could earn your sheep a higher placing.

43

Experienced showmen choose animals with heads that are long but of medium width. The neck should be long, slender and clean. A clean neck is free of excess wrinkles or folds of skin that can take away from the animal's general appearance.

Show sheep should hold their neck, head, and ears in an alert position. Stay away from those who walk around with their heads hanging down. Those animals may not feel well. During fly season, however, they may be holding their heads down to escape the flies.

Nature usually puts like things together. Sheep with long heads and necks usually have other body parts that are also long. They have longer legs, rumps, and loins. Short-necked animals usually have shorter legs and bodies.

There is a direct relationship between the length of an animal's neck and its loin length. The neck length measurement is usually the same as that of the loin length to within 1/2 inch. A long loin is important because the loin is the most expensive part of a lamb.

The neck measurement is taken from a point just behind the ears to where the neck and shoulder join.

FRONT STANCE
A wide front stance means the animal is heavier in the front than in the back, and has excess fat forcing the front legs apart. Sheep should be wider in the rear than in the front because most high priced cuts come from the back half of the animal.

44

Looking down on sheep from above, they should have more of a wedge-shape, being slightly narrower in the front than the back. Sheep with front legs that are as wide or wider apart than their rear legs have little rear muscling.

FRONT END
Sheep should be trim in the front end. Their brisket should not be heavy or wide and the brisket should blend well into the shoulders and front legs. The shoulders should be smooth and not stick out like wings.

TOP AND BOTTOM LINE

The topline of a sheep is the area of the back from the neck to the dock. The topline should be level, thick, and muscular. The topline should not sag. Sagging is a weakness caused by a lack of muscling along the back bone, rib, and loin areas.

The animal should have a fairly level underline. This means that the stomach should look trim and fairly level. A pot-bellied lamb over 6 months of age is usually carrying a lot of internal fat. In a younger lamb, it usually means it is getting too much roughage and not enough grain

BODY LENGTH

When given a choice between a structurally correct short or long-bodied sheep, pick the longer body. Animals with longer bodies have a greater proportion of meat in their more expensive hind saddle (rear half) area.

HIND SADDLE
The hind saddle is the loin and rump portions taken together.

The loin area is from between the last (back) two ribs to the hip bone. The last rib, called the short rib, is part of the loin. The rump area is from the hip bones to the tail dock joint.

The hind saddle should be more that half the overall length of the backline. To find out if this is true, you need to measure the hind saddle and the overall length.

The hind saddle is measured by placing the end of a yard stick between the last two ribs and measuring from there to the tail dock joint.

The overall length is measured by placing the end of a yard stick at the base of the neck. The lamb's head should be held in a natural, upright position. Measure along the back bone back to the tail dock joint.

The hind saddle measurement should be more that half the overall length measurement.

Measure the loin, rump, and hind saddle and use these measurements to compare sheep that are the same age.

DOCK

The dock area should be square and high. A sloping dock is a sign of poor muscling and excess fat in the dock area. Ewes with low set docks often urinate on themselves. This can lead to skin irritation and fly strike.

REAR STANCE

A sheep's rear legs should be wider apart than the front legs. This allows for more muscle development in the rear legs. Animals with good rear leg muscling usually carry good muscling throughout their body. The leg muscle should be full and deep and protrude on the outside of the leg.

Sufficient width between the rear legs is important for breeding animals. It allows the necessary width for large testicles in a breeding ram and a large full udder in a breeding ewe. Good rear leg width in ewes also means a wider pelvic area and easier lambing.

BODY CAPACITY
Lambs should be moderately deep in the front and in the rear flanks and be deeper from their top line to their underbelly line than they are wide. This allows enough body capacity for them to convert forage into weight gain. Large capacity also lets a ewe carry larger multiple lambs.

FLEECE
The fleece of sheep used in purebred breeding classes should be free of dark fiber or they may be placed low in the class. Dark fiber is usually not considered a fault in market lamb classes.

MUSCLING
Good muscling in meat-breed lambs is very important, whether they are shown in a market class or breeding class.

The best way to determine the muscling of a market lamb is by checking the width and thickness of its loin and the thickness of the muscling in its legs as compared to other lambs of the same age. A heavily muscled lamb will stand slightly wider in the rear than the front.

A large loin-eye is well-shaped and deep at the edges.

MUSCULAR-MEATY SHEEP

Muscles down the top of a meatless lamb are flatter and more shallow at the edges.

POORLY-MUSCLED SHEEP

The above illustrations show cross-sections in the loin area of a meaty muscular sheep and one that lacks meat or muscle. The bone size is the same in both sets of illustrations.

Look for a grooved top running along the back bone from the neck to the tail dock. The grooved top is made by a smooth roll of muscle on each side of the backbone. The lamb has good muscling in the loin area if this muscle feels large and round.

Select lambs that have good leg muscling. The same muscle that extends along the backbone also reaches almost to the hock in the lower part of the leg. Muscling in the leg is seen as a natural bulge.

Check the plumpness of the rear leg muscle by putting your hands around the leg and across the outside and inside thigh muscle. Lambs should also have some muscling in the front legs and shoulders as well as the rear legs.

FINISH OR CONDITION

The amount of fat cover that forms over the meat and muscle on a sheep's body is referred to as finish in a market lamb and condition in a breeding animal.

The meat market today wants lean, low-fat lambs. Judges will look closely to the amount of fat on your lamb.

If you select a lamb that is already close to having the proper finish or fat cover, the lamb would then be too fat by the time your show took place. When you look at lambs, be sure that you look ahead to what they should weigh by show time.

The next section will show you how to judge a lamb's finish or condition.

FIELD SCORING

Have someone hold onto a lamb for you. Keeping the three middle fingers of one hand close together, place them on the lambs back. The middle finger should be placed on the spine of the lamb with the index and ring finger closely placed on either side.

With the fingers close together, press all three fingers firmly down and move them down the lamb's spine (backbone). The three fingers will stay about level on a lamb that has a proper finish and is ready for market or showing in a breeding class. Whenever the index and ring finger are higher than the middle finger, the lamb is over finished and is carrying too much fat cover.

You should select lambs that are still a little under-finished. This would mean that your index and ring finger would be slightly lower than the middle finger. Beginners shouldn't select lambs with sharp backbones. You may not be able to get enough weight and finish on the lamb by show time.

Feed your lambs according to the amount of finish desired not according to what you think they should weigh.

Field score them constantly to keep an eye on their finish. This practice will avoid pushing small frame lambs to such a heavy weight that they are over-finished by show time. Not feeding a large frame lamb according to its condition score however can result in an under-finished lamb.

SEX OF LAMBS
The sex of the lambs you choose for showing will be determined by the rules of the fairs or shows that you plan to attend. Some shows only allow wethers to be shown in market lamb classes. It is important to check the rules of the shows you plan to attend before you select your lambs.

Wether lambs (castrated male lambs) and ram lambs have some advantages over a ewe (female) lamb. Wethers and ram lambs handle stress easier than ewe lambs. They also gain faster and develop muscle more easily without becoming over-fat.

There may be times however when choosing at least one ewe lamb and one wether would be better than having two wethers. Beginners sometimes become very attached to their lambs. If you are required to sell your lamb at the show, the wether can be sold and the ewe lamb taken back home to be raised into a breeding ewe.

If there are no rules prohibiting the showing of ewe lambs in a market class, the selection of a ewe lamb may be useful at sale time. Ewe lambs bring as much money as wether lambs, and ewe lambs are easier to sell after the show season as breeding stock.

FRAME SIZE
The frame size of a lamb is the build or shape of the lamb's skeleton.

If you are young or this is your first year showing sheep, it might be better to choose a medium frame lamb.

It will be easier for you to control and show a smaller framed lamb.

A lamb's frame size controls its correct market weight. This is important if you are showing in a market lamb class.

If the ideal market weight for a show is 110 to 125 pounds, a small frame lamb may be too fat at 110 pounds. Large frame lambs reach their correct finish at much heavier weights than do small frame lambs.

You need to use frame size to project what you think a lamb's weight will be when it is finished. Don't select small, short legged or fat lambs.

AGE AND WEIGHT OF LAMB

We have always found that lambs selected as show lambs do better if they are at least 60 days old. The lambs should have been weaned from their mother for at least two weeks to reduce stress to the lambs and prevent illness.

The lambs should be on a grain concentrate and be full-fledged ruminants (chewing their cud)

You can see a lamb chewing its cud. Watch the lamb when it is lying down. You will see his throat move as the food comes up from the stomach into the mouth. The lamb will chew for a while and then swallow the chewed food or cud. The lamb will repeat this several times.

Newly weaned lambs that are not chewing their cud can not digest grains well and may develop upset stomachs when you start feeding them grain.

The age of the lamb you select depends on their sex. Ram and wether lambs grow faster than ewe lambs. Select ewe lambs that are older than rams and wethers.

Lambs born in December and January are usually selected for May and June market lamb shows. Lambs born in December and January would be over weight and too fat for fall shows.

February and early March lambs are used for July and August market lamb shows. April lambs are normally seen at the fall market lamb shows.

Find out how much the lambs are gaining each day. Knowing whether a lamb is gaining 1/2 LB or 1 LB of weight per day will help you choose the lamb you need for your shows.

Good lambs gain at least 1/2 pound of weight per day. Large frame lambs and purebred lambs from meat breeds such as the Suffolk and Hampshire breeds often gain 3/4 to over 1 pound of weight per day. Crossbred lambs who are a cross of two meat breed purebreds will gain close to the same rate as the purebred.

Select 60-90 pound lambs for a show 80-90 days in the future.

Most judges prefer lambs who weigh between 115 to 125 pounds. Select lambs that have large enough frames that they do not become over finished (fat) before they reach these weights.

The chart below will help you decide the best beginning weight for your lambs. The finished weights should be adjusted for lambs that are gaining more or less weight per day.

ESTIMATED SHOW WEIGHT
FOR LAMB GAINING 1/2 LB PER DAY

Days Until Show	60	80	100
Beginning Wt.	Wt.	Wt.	Wt.
60 lbs	90 lbs	100 lbs	110 lbs
65 lbs	95 lbs	105 lbs	115 lbs
70 lbs	100 lbs	110 lbs	120 lbs
75 lbs	105 lbs	115 lbs	125 lbs
80 lbs	110 lbs	120 lbs	130 lbs

WHERE TO BUY A LAMB

If your family doesn't raise sheep, you will need to buy lambs for your project. Lambs are sold several different ways.

Lambs can be purchased directly from a farmer or producer (private treaty). You and your parents can pick out several sheep farms to visit and select your lambs at one of these farms.

If you go to a farm to buy your lambs, ask to see all of the lamb crop and not just the ones that have been selected to sell. This will give you an idea of the quality of the producer's lambs. If the producer has kept back all of the best lambs for himself, it may be better to buy your lambs from a different place.

A second way of purchasing lambs is to buy them through purebred, breeding stock, and club auctions.

These lambs usually must meet a certain conformation and health standard to be sold. Auctions give you the chance to see many lambs together.

Sheep sold through auctions are usually washed and trimmed. You will find it is easier to check the conformation of a washed and trimmed lamb.

Don't be afraid to climb into a pen and handle a lamb to check the conformation. The best way to compare lambs is by "hands on judging". You will learn how to do this later in this section of the book.

AUCTION SALE

SIGHT AND HANDS-ON JUDGING
Now that you have decided the size, age and weight of the lambs that you need, and have learned what is considered good and bad structure and conformation, you are ready to go shopping for lambs.

You will first judge the lambs by sight only. Then you will judge the lambs by handling them and comparing one lamb to another.

Producers should be willing to help you handle their lambs. However, if you are at a show and sale, the producer will want you to wait until after the show. Handling the lambs before a show could ruin a trimming job and cause the lamb to place lower in the class.

If a breeder objects to you handling his sheep after they have been placed in a sale order, eliminate his animals from your list of possible choices.

You should use both sight and hands-on judging any time you are selecting from a group of lambs.

SIGHT JUDGING
Sight judging is a method used to eliminate all but a few lambs in the group of animals you are considering.

Look at the group as a whole. Watch for any that immediately get your attention. If there are many animals together, have the first few that get your attention separated from the others. For some reason these animals caught your eye and made a good impression on you.

The first animals to catch your eye are often the same ones who have style or a showy look. This means they have an attractive profile and are upheaded and alert. They have what is called "eye appeal".

"EYE APPEAL" -- ATTRACTIVE, UPHEADED, ALERT

Allow the lambs to move around as a group. Look for and remove any that appear unhealthy such as having a cough, runny nose, watery or crusty eyes, or squinting. Also remove any who lack obvious structural soundness, are limping, or who walk with jerky movements.

HANDS ON JUDGING

Next, remove each animal individually from the remaining group. Have someone hold the animal's head for you.

Beginning at the head, check the animal's mouth for a correct bite. Is its teeth flush with the dental pad? Now check its eyes. Are the lids and whites of the eyes pink, not inflamed (red) or pale?

Look at the animal's feet. Are the pasterns strong looking and of medium length? Is it standing well up on its toes as it should be or is it down on its pasterns? During the motion of walking, are the front feet being placed straight out in front of its body and the rear feet straight under its body as they should be or are they being thrown out to the sides?

When the animal is standing still, is its back straight and level all the way to its dock? Is it longer than it is tall with good length of body?

Does the animal have a high dock and good width between its rear legs? Is it tight-hided meaning no loose skin or wrinkles? Do all of the body parts blend together smoothly?

Select a first, second, and third choice. Frequently, the one that first caught your eye will become your first choice unless a fault or structural weakness is uncovered. Now you should judge these three animals by using what you have learned under the structure and conformation section.

Select the animal you think is the closest to "the perfect animal".

PRICE OF LAMBS

What do show lambs cost? How much should you pay? Show lambs, including market and breeding class lambs, sell anywhere from market prices to several hundred dollars for purebred lambs.

You should expect to pay more than market prices. You need to show lambs that are better than the average market lamb if you want to place high in a show class.

Top quality market lambs cost more to raise because top quality rams and ewes are used to produce them. Registered purebred lambs cost even more.

Lambs from producers known for their ability to produce fast-gaining lambs will cost more than market price.

If you are a beginner, it may be better to start with a medium priced lamb until you gain some experience feeding, fitting, and showing.

Some producers offer extras to youths who purchase sheep from them. This may be a gift at the time the animal is purchased such as a book about sheep, a halter, or a piece of equipment. Others may offer a bonus cash award for any animal that they produce who goes on to earn a championship ribbon.

Nothing pleases a breeder more than to see an animal he produced win in the show ring. His reward is the future sales that result from selling a winner.

THE HOME COMING

BEFORE TRANSPORTING

Animals are often moved great distances to their new homes. Some times, this may cause stress to the animals.

Vitamin B Complex helps reduce stress. Give your sheep an injection of Vitamin B Complex just before loading or on the trailer after loading. They need 5cc per 100 pounds of body weight.

AVOIDING THE "SAFE SPACE"

All living creatures have an invisible bubble of space surrounding them that they consider to be "Safe Space". With sheep, this space is called their "fight or flight zone".

If something comes into a sheep's safe space they feel threatened and try to escape rather than fight. If they are unable to run away, they become nervous and stressed.

Sheep being herded may become afraid and nervous if enough space is not given to them.

Allowing more space between them and you creates less of a threat to the sheep and they soon calm down.

LOADING FOR TRANSPORT

Keeping in mind the "flight zone" or "safe space" of the lambs, set up panels to herd them onto the truck or trailer. Herding is much easier and less stressful than trying to move them by leading or physically dragging them down the alley of a sheep barn. Always handle sheep that are being transported as gently and as little as possible.

TRANSPORTING

Weather Conditions -- Be prepared for all weather conditions for the particular season of the year. Weather conditions frequently change abruptly. It's a good idea to provide side racks if sheep are being transported in an open truck. This enables them to stand up without being tied.

Provide a tarp or some other covering to shade the sheep from hot sun or an unexpected storm.

Temperature -- Sheep travel better during the cool of the day or at night whenever the weather is warm. If it is impossible to arrive at your destination before the heat of the day, stop as little as possible. Sheep travel well as long as air is moving across them to keep them cool.

Sheep transported during cool weather should be protected from air drafts. Use a tarp to prevent drafts and lay down a thick bed of straw for added insulation against the cold.

Vehicle Size And Ventilation -- Use a truck or trailer large enough for the size and number of sheep being transported. It is better to have too much space than not enough. Some window or open space should be provided for ventilation.

Safe Footing -- Provide safe footing for animals whenever they are transported to prevent injuries. The trailer or truck bed can become very slippery from urine and manure. A rubber pad, sand, or a heavy layer of straw or old hay work well to provide safe footing.

CARE UPON ARRIVAL

Unload your sheep in an area where you can watch them for a few days as soon as you arrive home. Move slowly and quietly around the unloaded animals.

Don't try to make friends with your sheep right away. Allow them time to settle in and get used to their new home.

Once the sheep have been unloaded, offer them free-choice alfalfa hay and watch them from a distance for a few minutes. Any that have become stressed by the trip will not eat and will look depressed (sad or sickly looking with droopy ears).

Give the sheep a few hours to recover from the trip and check on them again. Any that are still showing signs of feeling sick may need to be treated for transport stress (described below).

Animals that have been hauled for several hours shouldn't be given water until they have a chance to fill up on hay. This will take an hour or two. Don't let them drink large amounts of water at one time. Some times this causes diarrhea.

We give newly transported animals water that has had electrolytes added to it. Electrolytes in the water helps replace electrolytes lost from the stress of moving.

Use electrolyte products that contain bicarbonate of soda or some other buffering compound. Bovine Bluelite from Pipestone Veterinary Supply, Renew by AgriLabs, and Electrolytes Plus from Tri-Mutual Inc. are products containing buffering compounds.

TRANSPORT STRESS
Care given to newly purchased sheep directly before, during, and after being moved affects their health and well being. Those who become ill from stress usually develop signs of being sick within hours of being moved.

If any of the sheep acts sick, take their temperature and note any other symptoms that you see. An animal's temperature and its symptoms can help determine what illness it may be developing.

Ill sheep with a normal to slightly lower temperature may have transport tetany.

Sheep with temperatures above normal may be developing an infection and may need to be treated with antibiotics to help them recover.

If you think that the animal is ill, contact your veterinarian or follow the treatment suggested in a good sheep health care book.

CARE AFTER TRANSPORTING
Newly arrived sheep should not be handled for about two weeks other than for the preventive care described earlier. Management practices such as deworming, castrating, hoof trimming, shearing, and vaccinations should be postponed until after they are used to their new home.

CLIMATIC CONSIDERATIONS
Sheep need a little time to become used to the climate of their new home. Changes in humidity, temperature, and elevation can affect them. For example, sheep raised in the mountains may suffer from heat stress when placed in a new home in the South.

Sheep raised in lower elevations need a period of time to get used to higher elevations. These animals may appear to have difficulty breathing in thinner air. It is a well-known fact that athletes in training for the Olympics have difficulty getting used to higher elevations unless they undergo a period of adjustment.

Place the sheep in housing where cool air can move across them during hot weather. If air movement is low, put a fan on them.

SOCIAL NEEDS
Sheep are social animals. They like to be with other sheep. Have you noticed how sheep stay within sight of each other when they are grazing? It is rare to see a sheep off by itself unless it is ill.

Lambs are healthier and gain better when they are raised with other lambs. You should select a second lamb to be raised with your show lamb even if the second lamb is not going to be shown.

ADJUSTING TO NEW FEEDS

Sheep settle into a new home better whenever disruptions in their care and feeding are kept low. Slowly change them over to the feed mix you plan to use during the training and showing period.

To change the animals over to a new feed mixture, combine together 3/4 of the old feed mix with 1/4 of your new feed mix. Give them this mixture for about 3 days. On day 4 through day 6, mix 1/2 of the old feed with 1/2 of the new feed mix. On day 7 through 10, combine 1/4 of your old feed mix with 3/4 of your new feed mix. On day 10, the sheep can be given your new feed mix exclusively.

If you can't determine the amount or kind of feed the animal was used to getting, feed it only hay for 48 hours. After this time, begin feeding 1/4 pound of your grain mix to each animal per day. Increase the amount of grain by 1/4 pound per day until the animal is getting the desired amount of grain for its weight or age.

CARE AND FEEDING FOR SHOW

KEEPING SHOW SHEEP HEALTHY

Good care and proper nutrition will prevent most illnesses of show sheep. It is much easier to prevent illness than it is to treat for it.

Having healthy sheep requires being safety conscious and practicing preventive medicine. These are the two best medicines in the world. Show lambs grow and gain better if they are kept healthy.

Following a program of vaccination and disease prevention is a necessary part of preventive medicine.

Preventive medicine includes a good feeding program, fresh water, fly control, exercise, climatic control, hoof trimming, and keeping sheep free of stress and internal parasites (worms and coccidia).

SHEEP SAFETY

Just as people make their homes safe whenever babies are around, it is important to make your sheep's home safe. Be aware of possible dangerous conditions for your animals around the barn, feed area, pens, and pastures.

Sheep are naturally curious. They investigate everything, especially things that are shiny or that can be moved about.

Look for loose boards, nails, wire, rope, string, etc., that could cause injury to the animals.

Baling twine, string, and rope should not be left lying around. A sheep can get a piece of baling twine or string wrapped around its leg tight enough to cut off circulation.

Sheep like to chew on electric wires. Electric wires within reach should be covered with a piece of PVC pipe or a rubber hose that has been slit and fitted over the wires.

Check to make sure that feeders and water tubs are tip-proof. If you use buckets to feed or water your sheep, tie them securely so that an animal cannot get the bucket over its head.

Don't house your animals in an area where machinery or feed is stored. They can easily injure themselves on many kinds of machinery. Feed should be kept in an area that can be locked up. Sheep can become bloated and sick from eating large quantities of grain products.

Finally, do not leave your sheep alone while they are tied up or while on a grooming stand. More than one animal has gotten into trouble because its owner wasn't around when it got tangled up in a lead line or fell from a grooming stand.

PREVENTIVE MEDICINE

After animals have been given a couple of weeks to recover from being transported, and have gotten used to their new home, they need to be handled. Vaccinate them for overeating, pneumonia, and soremouth. It is also desirable to deworm, shear, and trim their hooves at this time.

VACCINATIONS
Show sheep should be vaccinated against certain diseases.

Sheep should not be vaccinated if they are sick. Vaccinations given to sick animals are not very effective because their immune system is lowered by the illness and they are unable to produce antibodies to the vaccinated disease.

The stress to the animal is reduced if the weather is clear and sunny at the time it is vaccinated.

OVEREATING VACCINATION
All sheep should be vaccinated for overeating with Clostridium Perfringens Type C and D toxoid two weeks after arrival. If this is their first vaccination, or if

you are not sure they received a first vaccination, they will need a second inoculation or booster shot 3 to 4 weeks later to give them full immunity.

It is best to vaccinate for overeating by injecting the vaccine subcutaneously. We prefer to use the loose skin of the neck. It is better not to give show sheep injections in their legs or rump. Sometimes injection sites become infected and you would not want it to be in an area of high priced cuts.

PNEUMONIA VACCINATION
A common illness seen in show sheep is respiratory infection which can lead to pneumonia. The disease can be controlled through certain preventive practices.

Before sheep can come down with a severe case of pneumonia, three things must be present. These include a virus, bacteria, and stress. It is sometimes difficult to protect them from all stresses and all types of bacteria. However, respiratory infections can be reduced or prevented by vaccinating for the most common virus related to cases of pneumonia.

Vaccinate the sheep with an IBR-PI3 **intra-nasal** cattle vaccine. Intra-nasal means into the nose. The powdered vaccine is combined with a fluid. It is then given through a small tube that is put into the nose of the animal and ejected. Recommended amounts are 1/4cc in each nostril for lambs and 1/2cc per nostril for adult sheep. The animal should be given the vaccine again about two weeks before it is taken to its first show.

SOREMOUTH VACCINATION

You only have to vaccinate for soremouth once in the animal's life time.

Soremouth is caused by an infectious and contagious virus. It is very important to vaccinate show animals against this disease if they haven't been vaccinated before. They probably will be exposed to soremouth sometime during the show season.

The soremouth virus is found in the scabs formed by the disease. Once these scabs fall off, they can infect the ground, show pens, and other equipment at show facilities. If a show animal gets a small scratch, it can become infected.

It will also be necessary to vaccinate all other animals on the premises because they can become infected from contact with either the show animals or the scab when it falls off.

The name of the vaccine used to vaccinate against soremouth is called ovine ecthyma vaccine. It is a live virus that can be spread even to humans.

The animal is vaccinated by painting the vaccine onto the scratched hairless skin under a front leg. A scab will form over the scratched area and after a short time the scab falls off.

Once an animal is exposed to the soremouth virus and gets the disease, it takes 2 or more weeks for it to get over it.

INTERNAL PARASITE CONTROL (Deworming)

Animals infected with internal parasites are less able to fight off disease and gain little if any weight. It is important to feed your sheep, not their internal parasites.

Show sheep should be dewormed two weeks after being moved to their new home and then every 3 to 4 weeks thereafter until show time.

Many different products are on the market that do very well to remove most worms that affect sheep. However, only a couple of deworming medications will remove tape worms. Although some claim that tapeworm infections are not harmful to sheep, like other worms they interfere with a lamb's ability to gain weight.

Dewormers approved for sheep are limited but most products that work well for cattle also work for sheep. If you decide to use one of the cattle dewormers, consult with your veterinarian and follow the label directions for cattle on a weight basis as to the amount to be given.

During the show season, sheep should be dewormed every 3 weeks if the product used is Tramisol or Safeguard. They only need dewormed every 4 weeks if Ivomec is used. The following dewormers are those most often used by sheep producers.

Tramisol -- It comes in a drench, paste, bolus, or injectable form and works well for all worms except tapeworms. The injectable form causes irritation at the injection site.

Safeguard -- This comes as a paste or a drench. This product works well on all worms and will remove most tapeworms if given at two to three times the label dosage. It is very safe even at higher than suggested label amounts.

Ivomec -- This product is available in drench or cattle injectable form. Ivomec works well on all worms except tapeworms. The product has a longer killing effect on worms than other dewormers. The injectable form causes irritation at the injection site.

Valbazen -- This product comes as a paste or drench. It is the only product on the market known to remove all tapeworms as well as the other worms.

SHEARING

Removing the wool from show sheep reduces stress during hot weather. This is especially important for market lambs who are on full feed. Market lambs cut back on the amount they eat if they become stressed by the heat.

Sometimes sheep clubs gather all their club's lambs together and have a shearer come in and shear all the lambs at one time. If you plan to show sheep more than one season, you may want to invest in electrical clippers and learn to shear your own animals.

Shearing equipment can be purchased from the following animal supply catalogs:

Sheepman Supply Co.
P.O. Box 100
Barboursville, VA 22923   1-800-336-3005

S. B. Wallace & Co.
P.O. Box 87
Marlinton, WV 24954   1-800-233-6914

Sheepman Supply sells a "Sheep Shearing Techniques" video and gives you a FREE detailed "how to" shearing chart with each purchase of Oster equipment. The chart is big enough to but on the barn wall and read while you are shearing.

SHEARING EQUIPMENT

If you plan to purchase shearing equipment, I would recommend buying shearing clippers with a 3-inch head. It offers more versatility and a wider cut with each stroke.

A comb commonly used to shear sheep is a 13-tooth thin comb. This comb is designed for close, smooth shearing. It leaves a fairly smooth finish to the clipped wool and is used for general shearing.

A 20-tooth goat comb designed for regular clipping of the belly of breeding stock and slick shearing of market lambs is also available to fit the 3-inch clipper head.

The 20-tooth goat comb was originally designed to be used for shearing Angora goats. It is now also used by those raising, selling, and showing market lambs because it guarantees a close smooth shearing job.

The 20-tooth goat comb is a better choice for those who are inexperienced in shearing and fitting. It is safe enough to be used by kids and I have never heard of anyone leaving a shear cut on their animal from its use.

Don't make the mistake of purchasing the 20-tooth trimming and blocking comb. This particular comb should be used by experienced shearers and fitters because it has pointed teeth which can easily penetrate the skin. It is used to sculpt the top of the wool rather than to shear it down to the skin.

Whatever comb you use, the shearing job should leave the animal with a smooth appearance. Taking special care to get a smooth shearing job at this time will make your trimming job easier later on.

WHEN TO SHEAR
All sheep should be sheared early in the show season. If you purchase your show sheep, they should be sheared as soon as they are used to their new home.

81

Additional shearings will depend on your particular type of show.

MARKET CLASS LAMBS

Market lambs should be sheared monthly with a 3-inch 20-tooth goat comb. Shearing your market lambs throughout the growing and gaining period helps keep them cooler. Cool lambs have better appetites and gain more rapidly.

The most popular way to show a market lamb is slick shorn (sheared to the skin). They are sheared each month and again several days to a week before the show.

Lambs who will be shown with "breeches" should be slick sheared each month from the rear flanks forward but not sheared over the hips, rump and dock. "Breeches" is the wool left over the rump, dock, and rear legs. This wool is trimmed just before the show to create more shape to the legs and rump.

Showing lambs with "breeches" is described in detail in the trimming section of this book.

In some areas of the country, market lambs are fitted and trimmed like breeding sheep. Usually, the fleece must be less than 1 inch long at show time. In such cases, the lamb's last shearing takes place about 60 days before the show.

Check the rules for your particular shows.

BREEDING CLASS SHEEP

Meat Breeds -- Meat-type breeding class sheep may be shown slick shorn or with "breeches" like market lambs, or with longer wool that is carded and trimmed just before a show.

Carding and trimming are explained later in the book.

If you plan to card and trim your breeding sheep, their last shearing should be about 80 to 90 days before the first show. The fleece is then allowed to grow out until fitting time.

Wool Breeds -- The fleece of wool breeds is left longer for showing than that of the meat-type breeds. This is necessary so that the judge can better evaluate their wool. Usually, wool breeds are sheared no later than 120 days before the show to allow for enough wool growth. Check the requirements for your particular show.

GROOMING STAND SHEARING

The following directions are not those normally followed by experienced shearers. However, we have found this method works well for kids and inexperienced shearers with only a few sheep to shear.

It is also the same method used to slick shear market lambs with the 20-tooth comb. Detailed directions for slick shearing are given under the book section FITTING SHEEP FOR SHOWING.

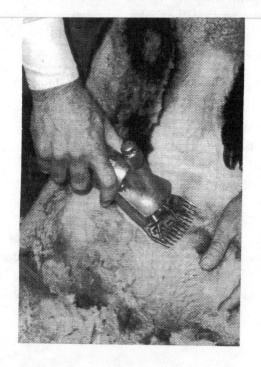

84

Before putting the sheep on the grooming stand, set it on its rump and shear its belly and the inside of the rear legs. Take care not to cut the ram's sheath or the ewe's teats.

The remainder of the shearing process will take place with the animal on a grooming stand. If you don't own a grooming stand, you should halter the animal and have someone restrain the sheep while you shear it.

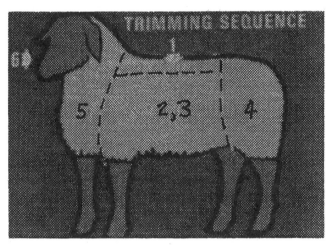

GROOMING STAND SHEARING ORDER

(1) -- Shear in long strokes. Begin shearing above the dock. Shear from this point to the base of the neck. The next shearing strokes along the back are in the same direction as the first and should be straight and parallel to the first stroke.

(2) & (3) -- The sheep's sides are sheared in the same direction as that used along the back. Shear from the rear of the animal to the front. Pull the skin tight with

85

your left hand as you shear with your right hand to get the smoothest possible shearing job. Reverse this if you are left-handed.

Keep your strokes straight and level. Sheep look longer when shearing strokes are kept straight and parallel to each other.

(4) & (5) -- The front and rear legs from the knee up are sheared in upward strokes next. This will prevent injuries to the legs. Animals with excessive amounts of lower leg wool may need the lower legs clipped as well.

(6) -- Finally, beginning at the point of the shoulder, shear forward and upward toward the head. Follow the same upward strokes and shear the brisket and neck. This will make the neck appear longer.

POODLE CLIPS
(Leaving Breeches Or Pants)
Some market lamb shows allow wool to be left longer over the rump. These sheep are sheared from the rear flanks forward each month beginning about 2 months before show time. They are not sheared over the hips, rump and dock.

The wool that is left on the rear of the lamb is blended in later to give the lamb a longer-bodied appearance with better balance and a fuller leg.

(1) -- Follow Step 1 and Step 2 in the directions given above for GROOMING STAND SHEARING.

86

(2) -- Shear down the back beginning from a point located in front of the hip bone to the base of the neck. Make parallel shearing strokes over the top and along the sides, leaving the wool on the hips, rump and dock.

(3) -- Follow Steps 5 and 6 listed above for GROOMING STAND SHEARING.

HOOF TRIMMING

Trim your sheep's hooves once a month with the last trimming a few days before a show. This will keep them standing correctly on their hooves and prevent hoof infections.

Begin by cleaning any mud or debris from the hoof. Carefully snip off and shorten the tips of each hoof toe gradually with a pair of hoof trimmers. By trimming the toes back gradually, you will avoid cutting them back so short that blood is drawn.

Next, trim off the excess hoof growth from the outer wall of the hoof that has overgrown the sole. A pocket knife can be used to create a smoother more level job if you wish.

The wall and sole of a trimmed hoof should be left smooth with no cracks in it. The hoof should be trimmed flat, leaving enough hoof wall to offer solid support. The hoof wall should be short enough to make contact with the ground but still offer protection to the soft sole of the foot.

TRIMMING HOOVES

If the hooves are too overgrown, they will need to be trimmed in stages with a week or two between trimmings. Do not trim the hoof so short that blood is drawn. This may make the foot sore and cause the animal to limp.

FEEDING

If you have chosen a structurally correct healthy lamb, its further development will be determined by your feeding program. The better the job you do, the better the chances are that your lamb will earn a high placing in the showring.

The amount and kind of feed a lamb should get will depend upon its weight, maturity and the number of days until show time.

If you are inexperienced at feeding market lambs or a beginner in the lamb program, you should consult such authorities as Vo-Ag teachers, extension agents or breeders from your area on what grains or feed are available and which of these feeds work the best for putting weight on a lamb.

Extension agents and Vo-Ag teachers have the ability to create a feed mixture formula for you from readily available grains in your particular area.

Everyone has a feed formula that they claim works well to put weight on lambs. The one that works the best is the one that lambs will eat and is high in energy and protein. Just like kids, lambs dislike anything that has a bitter taste.

NUTRITIONAL NEEDS
Lambs being fed to market weight need feeds that are high in protein. It takes protein to build muscle with little fat. We found that our Suffolk and Suffolk-cross lambs did well on a feed ration containing 15 to 16 per cent protein.

A suitable grain or feed ration for lambs must also be adequate in energy. Energy in a feed ration is sometimes listed as TDN (total digestible nutrients). Rations for lambs should contain 70 % to 80 % TDN.

Energy is the calorie part of a feed ration needed to keep a lamb gaining weight. Energy is first used by the lamb's body for simple maintenance. It is the fuel needed by the lamb to sustain life. This includes digestion, respiration, temperature regulation, muscular activity, and body tissue repair and replacement.

Most of the extra energy left in a feed ration that is not used for maintenance is used for growth, weight gain, and wool production.

An early sign of inadequate energy in the diet of a growing lamb is a reduction in the amount of weight it is gaining. Lambs and sheep often stop growing and lose weight if they are fed rations that are deficient in energy. Energy deficient animals are less resistant to disease and internal parasites.

A good feed ration should contain at least a 2 to 1 calcium to phosphorus ratio. Ammonium chloride or feed-grade lime should be added to their feed mixture to prevent urinary calculi when limited amounts of hay are fed to lambs on high concentrate feed rations.

The grains chosen to make up an ideal feed ration should ferment and degrade (deteriorate) in the rumen quickly to prevent indigestible fibrous material from collecting within the rumen. The grain or feed ration should be both tasty and economical. If the ration doesn't taste good, the lamb will not eat as much as it should to gain the right amount of weight.

The addition of lasalocid (Bovatec) to the feed ration aids in the prevention of digestive disturbances and acidosis, and helps prevent the growth of coccidia.

In addition to a concentrated feed ration, lambs should be given good quality roughage (hay) that degrades rapidly within the rumen. It should be one that is high in calcium. High-quality legume hays such as alfalfa fit both of these purposes.

Lambs also need free-choice fresh clean water and a sheep vitamin-mineral salt mix.

WHAT TO FEED
There are many very good prepared feed rations that can be purchased in loose or pelleted form that can be fed to sheep. Those who feed more than a few sheep often prepare their own feed ration from a mixture of several grains and supplements.

PELLETED FEED RATIONS
Some lamb feeders prefer to use a complete pelleted ration to feed out their lambs. A good high-energy complete pelleted feed ration commonly costs more than a loose grain ration. However, the ease of storage, handling, and savings in time may out weigh the extra cost.

Lambs may pick through loose grain mixtures, eating some parts and leaving others. My experience has been that whenever lambs do this, it is usually because the grain mixture has become stale, contaminated, or it isn't tasty.

Barley, corn, wheat, or oats that are processed into pellets can result in soft fat and reduced carcass quality. Unprocessed grain lessens this problem.

If you decide to feed a pellet to your lambs, make sure the diameter of the pellet is small. Lambs sometimes choke while eating pellets larger than 1/4 inch in diameter. Never use a horse or cattle pellet. Most are too large and many have copper in them.

A pelleted ration for lambs who weigh under 60 pounds should contain 18 % protein. The percentage of protein can be reduced to 14 % to 16 % once the lamb is over 60 pounds. The pellet should be high in energy containing 70 % to 80 % TDN.

LOOSE GRAIN RATIONS
Lambs need diets that ferment and deteriorate (degrade) rapidly within their rumen to be able to gain and grow well. Corn often makes up the greatest percentage of most feed mixtures because it is higher in energy and ferments more rapidly within the rumen than oats and barley. Oats and barley, because of their hulls, are high in indigestible material. This material may cause a lamb to become pot-bellied.

Soybean meal and peanut meal are often the most used sources of protein added to grain mixtures to increase and supply the proper amount of protein.

Vitamins A, D and E and minerals are usually added to grain mixtures that use loose meal as a source of protein.

Another source of protein that can be added to a whole grain mixture is a commercial pelleted protein supplement. Many protein supplements contain vitamins, minerals, and sometimes a coccidiostat.

FEED RATION FORMULAS
The following formulas are rations that can be mixed which contain about 14 % to 16 % protein. Some of these rations have lower energy values than others because they contain little or no corn. Rations of this type are often used to feed lambs through the summer heat for shows that take place in the fall.

If a lamb isn't gaining weight with enough finish from one of these formulas, the energy or TDN in the ration may be too low. Should this happen, add or increase the amount of corn in the ration gradually while decreasing the same amount of oats or barley in it. Lambs that are putting on too much fat too quickly should have some of the corn in their ration decreased and replaced with oats or barley.

Don't constantly make changes in the kind of feed you give your lambs once they are used to a particular kind of feed. Changes, especially those that are drastic or made too quickly, may cause digestive upsets or cause them to stop eating. If you must make a change in the ration, do it slowly over several days or weeks.

Ingredient	Rations				
	1	2	3	4	5
	lbs	lbs	lbs	lbs	lbs
Barley, rolled	20				
Corn, whole			40		50
Corn, cracked	20	62	40	40	27.5
Oats, rolled	30	12.25		40	
Protein Pellet	10			10	
Soybean Meal		18	17		17
Molasses, dry or liq.		05	02.5	02.5	05
Wheat Bran	19.5			07	
Feed-grade lime	00.5	01.5	00.5	00.5	0.5
Plain Salt		01.0			
Ammonium Chloride		00.25			
Total in pounds	100	100	100	100	100

Adding lasalocid to loose grain rations helps prevent coccidia. We prefer a product called Bova Mix from Pipestone Veterinary Supply. It comes in 5 lb bags which is added to one ton of grain mixture. This would be 1/4 lb to 100 lbs of grain mixture.

We add 1,000,000 IU Vitamin A, 250,000 IU Vitamin D, and 2,000 IU Vitamin E to 100 lbs of our grain ration. We also have a top quality sheep vitamin-mineral salt mixture available to the lambs on a free-choice basis. A vitamin-mineral premix such as Pipestone's Micro Mix could be used in place of this if you wished.

Whenever salt, vitamins, and minerals are not included in the grain ration, it is important to have a free-choice sheep vitamin and mineral-salt mix available to the lambs at all times.

After you decide what type feed to give your lambs, purchase enough of the grain mixture or pelleted feed to last for the entire feeding period. There can be slight differences in the flavor of pellets and feeds prepared or mixed at different times.

By purchasing all the feed needed for the entire feeding period, you will prevent digestive disturbances in your animals. It will also avoid the possibility of running out of feed during a time when the feed store is closed.

To provide enough feed for each lamb during the feeding period, you should figure about 4 pounds of feed per day for each lamb.

Once lambs are put on feed, it is important not to change the type, amount, or time of day when the animals are fed.

HAY

Show sheep should have access to the best possible hay along with their grain or pelleted feed. Use a bright green leafy alfalfa. Good quality alfalfa hay is a good source of calcium and keeps the sheep's rumen working well. This helps prevent digestive upsets and helps keep the animal on feed and eating well. Other types of hay are often too stemmy and are poorer sources of fiber and nutrients.

The amount of hay you give to your show animals will depend on the amount of time before your main show. Many allow show lambs free-choice alfalfa hay from the beginning of the feeding period until about 30 days before the show. At that time, most lambs should weigh close to 100 pounds.

About 30 days before the show, gradually reduce the amount of hay each lamb gets each day until you are feeding each of them about 1 lb of alfalfa hay twice a day. Ten days before the show, reduce the hay to 1/2 lb twice a day.

If 3 to 4 days before the show it looks as though a lamb has a hay belly (potbelly), reduce its hay to about 1/2 lb per day until show time.

Lambs not getting hay at least twice a day frequently chew on anything made of wood and sometimes even pull wool out of their penmates. They also usually suffer from a loss of appetite and weight gain. These conditions can be reversed in about two weeks by feeding lambs about 1 lb of alfalfa hay twice a day.

MINERAL-SALT MIX
A complete **sheep** vitamin-mineral-salt mixture should be available to lambs and other show sheep at all times. Rams and wether lambs especially need the salt found in these mixes to force them to drink water. This along with adequate calcium will help prevent urinary calculi.

It is important that you only use vitamin-mineral-salt mixtures that are meant to be fed to sheep. Many other livestock mixtures contain only trace minerals and often have copper in them. **Anything containing copper shouldn't be fed because copper is toxic to sheep.**

WATER

Clean fresh water is very important to the health and growth of sheep. Sheep drink more water during hot weather and whenever they are getting a high-protein feed ration.

Lambs will cut back on the amount of feed and hay that they eat if fresh cool water isn't available to them at all times. If a lamb eats less than it should because of a lack of fresh water, it will not gain weight well.

The water container should be emptied and refilled with fresh, cool, clean water at least twice each day during warm weather. The container should be thoroughly washed and cleaned at least once a week and twice a week during warm weather.

Sometimes show animals refuse to drink water at a show because it tastes different to them than what they have been drinking at home. The difference in the flavor of the water may be from fluoride, chemicals, or minerals that they are not used to tasting in their water.

Add something to the sheep's drinking water at home and at the show to disguise the taste to prevent them from refusing to drink water at the show. About two to three weeks before taking the animals to a show, add an electrolyte mix to their water. This gives them time to get used to the taste.

This same electrolyte can then be added to their water at the show. We like to use electrolytes in the water because they help replace electrolytes that are lost from the animal's body from the stress of hauling, fitting, and showing

We prefer electrolyte products that contain a source of bicarbonate such as Renew, Electrolytes Plus, or Bovine Bluelite. Other products used by some for this purpose are Resorb or Biolyte. Vanilla extract or Gatorade can be used to disguise the taste of the water. If you use vanilla extract, add only a couple of drops of it to the water at home and at the show.

FEEDING METHODS
There are two methods of feeding out lambs, the hand-fed and self-fed methods. We prefer the hand-fed over the self-fed method because it gives you the chance to check on the animals twice a day. This provides you an opportunity to pick up on any health problems early on. One of the first signs of a sick lamb or sheep is a lack of appetite.

Hand-feeding is the most common method used. With this method, the lambs are fed a measured amount of feed two or more times each day.

The self-feeding method allows lambs to eat feed free-choice or whenever they desire. Normally lambs fed this way have been on free-choice feed since shortly after birth.

99

FEED CONTAINERS

Always feed from a clean feeder, never on the ground. This prevents sheep from being infected with bacteria, worms, and coccidia (a type of internal parasite).

The feed container for animals being hand-fed should be cleaned out each time they are fed. This makes sure the animals get clean fresh feed each time. This is especially important during the summer time when feed can become stale. Lambs often will not eat stale feed or feed that has been slobbered on by other lambs.

If a grain mixture is used in a self-feeder, it shouldn't be allowed to become stale. Put enough feed in the self-feeder to last for only 24 hours.

FEEDER SPACE

Some sheep are shy about pushing their way into a feeder to get their fair share of feed. They often don't gain weight as well as more aggressive animals unless there is a large amount of space at the feeder.

When hand-feeding, make sure that each animal has a large enough space at the feeder so that all are able to eat at the same time. Feeder space required for each animal is at least 18 inches.

FREQUENCY OF FEEDING
Feed sheep at the same time, in the same feeder, and in the same area each time they are fed. Hand-fed animals should be fed at least twice a day. This lets their digestive system make better use of the feed they have eaten.

Feeding animals more often than once a day reduces the chances that they will suffer from a digestive upset. It encourages them to clean their feed up in a shorter period of time because the feed is clean and not stale from sitting in a feeder. Feeding more often also makes sure that each animal gets its share of feed.

A couple of days before leaving for your show, gradually cut back on the amount of feed given the lambs to about 2/3 of what they are used to getting each day. This will prevent digestive upsets and helps keep them on feed while at the show.

WEIGHING FEED
A scale to weigh feed is necessary if you plan to use the self-feeding method of feeding your lambs or sheep. A

small hanging scale or vegetable scale can be purchased for this purpose.

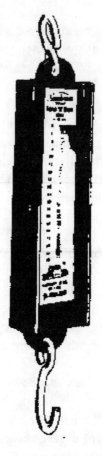

FEED SCALES

It is important to know the amount of feed you are giving your animals. Each time you feed them, weigh their feed so that you know the exact amount they are getting.

Weighing the feed given to animals helps avoid the possibility of giving them an unaccustomed amount of feed which could cause digestive disturbances. By weighing the feed, you also will know how much extra feed to measure out if you decide to increase the amount they are being fed.

AMOUNT TO FEED

Feeding a market or show lamb to reach the right amount of finish by a particular time is an art. Knowing when to increase or decrease how much feed your lamb should get many times will depend on how thin or fat the lamb is. No matter which feeding method is used, you will constantly need to check the finish on the lamb.

HAND-FEEDING

Most authorities use 3 % to 4 % of a lamb's body weight as a rule of thumb as to the amount of feed they should get each day. Lambs shouldn't be fed more feed than they can consume in one hour's time.

Please see the hand feeding chart on the next page.

Hand-feeding Chart

Daily Amounts Needed Based On 3 % to 4 % Body Weight

Lamb	Hay		Feed	
Weight	Morning	Evening	Morning	Evening
60 lbs	Free choice	Free choice	20 oz	20 oz
70 lbs	Free choice	Free choice	22 oz	22 oz
80 lbs	Free choice	Free choice	28 oz	28 oz
90 lbs	Free choice	Free choice	30 oz	30 oz
100 lbs	1 lb	1 lb	32 oz	32 oz
110 lbs	1 lb	1 lb	32 oz	32 oz
120 lbs	1/2 to 1 lb	1/2 to 1 lb	32 oz	32 oz

SELF-FEEDING

Most lambs that are fed using the self-fed method are given a pelleted feed. Lambs receiving a pelleted feed ration should also have access to free choice alfalfa hay until about 30 days before the show.

After that time, gradually cut back on the amount of hay over the next two to three weeks until the lambs are getting about 1 pound each of hay daily just before the show.

Lambs are allowed the free-choice feed until about one week before the show or until they are within 10-15 pounds of the desired show weight. At that time, they are hand-fed twice a day until show time.

104

INDIVIDUAL FEEDING
Sometimes when all lambs are fed together out of the same feeder some get too fat while others remain too thin.

Gaining Weight Too Rapidly -- A lamb that starts getting too fat may have to be separated from the others and fed less feed by itself to keep it from becoming too fat before show time. After feeding, turn the lamb back in with the other lambs.

Gaining Weight Too Slowly -- A healthy lamb that doesn't gain weight as fast as others being fed the same ration may be getting less of the feed. It may be smaller or less aggressive than the others. Feed this lamb in a separate pen from the others so that it is able to get its full share of feed. Again, turn the lamb back in with the other lambs after feeding.

LAMBS WHO STOP EATING
If a lamb stops eating feed, skip one feeding of grain for all of the lambs. Give them only good alfalfa hay. This will prevent any others from overeating on grain and getting sick. After skipping this one feeding of grain, give all of the lambs about 1/2 of their normal amount of ration at the next feeding. Gradually increase the amount of grain given to the lambs back up to the amount they were getting before one or more of them stopped eating.

Never make drastic changes in a lamb's grain ration. Don't increase the amount more than 1/4 pound for each lamb at each feeding. Wait about 3 to 4 days before increasing the amount again by another 1/4 pound. This will prevent any lambs from getting sick because they ate too much grain at one time.

Whenever lambs stop eating for more than one feeding, it is a sign that something is wrong. The lamb may have a more serious problem than simple indigestion. Tell an adult or your veterinarian whenever this happens and ask for their advice on treatment.

FLY CONTROL

Lambs being fed for a show usually have little or no wool cover. As the weather gets hot, flies may become a problem. It is important to keep the fly population down. Otherwise the lambs must constantly be fighting the biting flies. This causes the lambs to reduce the amount of time spent eating and they don't gain weight as well.

Lambs can get some relief from the biting flies if the haired areas of their body (legs and face) are sprayed or wiped with a fly repellent. Be careful not to get spray into the lamb's eyes.

Be sure to take your fly repellent with you to the show so that you can put fly repellent on the animal before it goes into the showring.

Fly control is harder if lambs are being fed feed mixtures containing molasses. The flies are attracted to the sweet smelling feed and the manure. We recommend reducing the amount of molasses or taking it out completely during fly season.

If flies become a problem, clean the bedding back to the ground. Put down a 1/2 inch layer of slaked lime over the ground. After the ground has been covered, put fresh bedding down over the lime. This helps with two problems. It reduces the odor and the moisture that draw flies.

WEIGHT GAIN AND FINISH

For lambs to end up at the proper weight and finish for the show, it is important to know how rapidly they are gaining weight. Lambs should be weighed; condition scored; and sheared every few weeks.

ANIMAL SCALES

WEIGHING YOUR LAMB
Weigh your lambs every two weeks and record their weights. This lets you know whether or not they are gaining well enough to be ready for your main show.

Weight loss or inadequate weight gain can be a sign that the lambs need an increase in the amount of feed given to them. Weight loss also can be a sign of a sick animal or a ration that is too low in energy.

Lambs also often lose weight if they aren't getting enough good quality hay. If lambs are leaving uneaten feed, perhaps something is wrong with their feed or their feed container.

Lambs gaining too quickly may need the energy reduced in their feed or the amount of feed they are receiving decreased slightly. You may have to exercise with them for a little longer than the others just to prevent them from getting too fat.

ESTIMATING WEIGHT WITHOUT A SCALE
If you only have one or two lambs, you may not have scales. This may prevent you from knowing your lambs' exact weight and rate of gain. This will also make it more difficult to determine if your lambs are reaching the correct weight for an upcoming show.

If you don't own a scale, you can get a fairly correct idea of a lamb's body weight from certain measurements. Measure the length and heart girth of the lamb and use these measurements in the following formula.

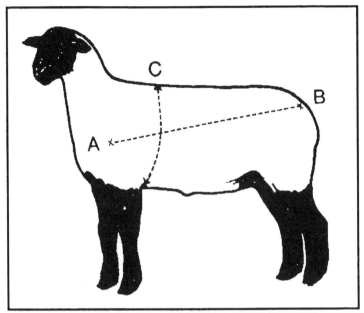

MEASURING HEART GIRTH AND LENGTH

Step 1 -- Measure the heart girth from slightly behind the shoulder blade, down over the fore ribs and under the body to behind the elbow (distance C in illustration).

Step 2 -- Measure the length of the lamb's body from the shoulder to the pinbone of the rump. (Distance A-B in illustration.)

Step 3 -- Take the measurements obtained in Steps 1 and 2 and apply the following formula to determine body weight:

Heart girth x heart girth x body length divided by 300 equals weight in pounds

Example: If a lamb's heart girth measures 32 inches and its body length measures 33 inches, how much does the lamb weigh?

32 x 32 = 1,024
1,024 x 33 = 33,792
33,792 divided by 300 = 112.6 lb

ESTIMATING FINISH OR CONDITION

Feed your show sheep according to the amount of finish (fat) you would like to have on them at show time not according to what you think they should weigh. This can be done by condition scoring the animal each time you weigh or measure it.

Knowing an animal's condition score lets you decrease or increase the amount of feed it is getting depending upon how fat or thin it is.

Condition scoring helps avoid pushing a lamb with a small frame to such a heavy weight that it is over-finished (too fat) by show time. It also avoids improperly finished large frame lambs who were not fed enough.

CONDITION SCORING

Condition scoring is a method of checking the amount of fat cover on lambs and sheep. In animals who have become too fat, a split can be felt over the tail head (dock). As the animal gets fatter, the split continues up the backbone. This split will keep on increasing up the back by about one inch a week.

110

Directions For Field Scoring: The field scoring method learned earlier to select a market lamb can be used to condition score your lambs. We feel this method is easier for young people to use.

To field score a lamb, press your three middle fingers down firmly along the lamb's spine. The area covered by these fingers should be nearly level in a properly finished lamb. The spinal bones can be felt only by exerting pressure. In a properly finished lamb, you will be able to count the lamb's ribs but they will not feel sharp.

If the middle finger is higher than the fingers to each side, the lamb still needs to gain more weight. If the middle finger is much lower than the fingers at each side, the lamb is getting too fat.

Directions For Condition Scoring: A more complicated method of checking an animal's finish involves feeling the sharpness or roundness of the backbone in the loin area and the crosswise bones lying under the loin area.

Sheep put fat on over the loin area and in the leg area last. This also is the first place fat is lost during weight loss. By feeling the bones in these areas, it is easier to determine the amount of fat the animal is carrying.

The scoring system that is described is used by many authorities. It assigns numbers based on a scale of 1.0 to 5.0. The scores relate to the amount of muscle and fat over the loin, above and behind the last rib.

A score of 1.0 is an extremely thin animal with less than 10% fat in or on its body. A 5.0 score indicates an excessively fat animal with 50% or more fat on its body. Both extremes are unhealthy.

To enable you to score the sheep without causing too much stress, pen them tightly so they can't get away from you as you feel their backs.

Place an opened hand crosswise on the lower portion of the animal's backbone, behind the ribs and ahead of the widest part of the hips. With the palm down, put your thumb on the animal's backbone. Squeeze down with your fingertips over the edge of the lower back (loin area).

Feel for the tips of the bones that jut to the side. Check to see if the bones that jut out to each side and protrude upward from the spine are sharp and easily felt or are round and hidden with fat and muscle.

By repeating this procedure on a few animals of about the same age, you will begin to detect differences in size and thickness of back muscles.

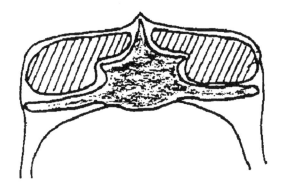

CONDITION SCORE 1

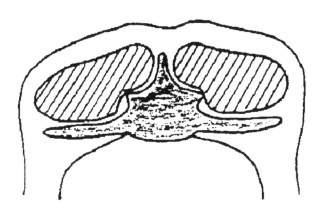

CONDITION SCORE 5

Score 0 -- An animal with this score is extremely thin. It's impossible to find any muscle or fat between the skin and the bones.

Score 1 -- The spine is prominent and sharp in animals carrying this condition. The rib bones have no fat covering. The bones that jut out to the side also are sharp and the fingers can easily press under the ends of the bone. A concave or depressed space is felt where the loin muscle should be.

Score 2 -- Animals with this score have a thin fat cover. The spine is still prominent but not extremely sharp. The rib bones have a corrugated feel to them rather than sharp and well defined. The fingers still go under the bones that jut out to the side but only with a little pressure. The loin region is moderately concave but still has little fat cover.

Score 3 -- The spine has a small elevation and feels smooth and rounded. The individual spinal bones can be felt only by exerting pressure. The ends of the bones that jut out are smooth and well covered. It takes hard pressure with the fingers to find the ends.

The loin muscle is fully developed with about 1/4 inch or less of overlying fat. The loin slopes downward from the midpoint of the back and extends to either side.

This is the ideal score.

Score 4 -- The spine can be detected only as a line down the back. The spinal bones can be detected with pressure as a hard line. The fat cover is thick. There is moderate bulging of the loin. The tips of the loin bones that jut out are hidden under more than 1/3 inch of fat and can't be felt.

Score 5 -- There's a depression or dimple over the spine. This is caused by the layers of fat lying on either side of the spinal column. The spinal bones aren't detectable even with firm pressure. Animals with this score have a fully developed loin muscle and thick overlying fat.

The loin bones are not felt either at the side or top of the loin except by deep pressure. Fat bulges over the edge of the loin and often there is large deposits of fat over the rump and tail dock.

EXERCISE OF SHOW ANIMALS

Exercise is important for animals on full feed. Turning your sheep out onto pasture for a couple of hours each day to allow them to run and play is good exercise. Probably the best exercise of all for sheep is walking.

WALKING WITH A HALTER

115

Sheep fed full feed should be walked about one-half to one mile twice a day. To be able to do this, it is important to halter break your animals as soon as possible. See TRAINING FOR THE SHOWRING elsewhere in the book for halter breaking and teaching animals to lead.

WHEN TO EXERCISE
The exercising of sheep should always be done during the coolest part of the day. Exercise during this time of day helps reduce stress on the animal and prevents it from getting sick. This is important during hot weather and especially in areas of the country that have humid climates.

FORMS OF EXERCISE
Don't expect your animals to do any form of exercise that you can't do with them. If you expect the animal to run, then you should run with it. If you want the animal to jump over hurdles, jump over them with the animal. By doing this, you will not force your sheep to exercise beyond their ability and endurance level to stay healthy.

I am a great believer of exercise for man and animal but I'm not convinced that forced exercise is as beneficial as leisure exercise. Forced exercise that is carried out over too long a period of time may cause more damage than good. It can create stress, especially in hot weather.

AMOUNT OF EXERCISE NEEDED

How much exercise is needed by animals is an often asked question. Too much exercise may cause an overuse of energy beyond that supplied by the amount of feed the animal is eating. This would reduce the amount of weight the animal gains. However, if show animals don't get any exercise, the extra feed that is eaten by them may turn to fat.

Begin exercising your lamb or sheep by walking with it 1/4 mile once a day. Gradually build up to about one mile twice a day.

If the animal begins to gain weight faster than you want it to gain, increase the distance it walks each day. If it isn't gaining weight fast enough, reduce how much exercise it gets each day.

INCREASING LEG MUSCLING

Building rear leg muscling at feeding time is done by using something sturdy for the animals to stand on with their front legs.

The feeder is placed high enough that they must use a step, a ramp, or cement blocks to stand upon with their front legs in order to be able to reach their feed. This causes most of their weight to rest on their rear legs and increases the size of the rear leg muscles.

The height of the front-leg step is increased gradually for lambs as they grow until the front feet are about 18 inches higher than the back feet.

A point that should be remembered by those who show
sheep is that no amount of exercise can make a
champion from a poor animal who originally lacked
muscling.

SIXTY DAYS BEFORE THE SHOW

SCHEDULING

SIXTY DAY CALENDAR

There will be many things that must get done during the last 6 to 8 weeks before your first show. To make it easier to remember when everything should be done, use a calendar. Mark the dates for all club meetings, clinics, final shearing, and weighing in of your animals, and finally the scheduled date for a veterinary examination.

Make sure to send transfer or registration papers into purebred organizations early enough that they can be returned to you if you are showing sheep in a purebred class. When they are returned, make sure they have been filled out accurately and in your name.

An examination of your show sheep by a veterinarian is necessary to get health papers for them. Don't forget to put down the date when health papers are needed and when entry papers for your sheep are due.

Mark the dates of shows in your area where you can go to observe.

Sixty days before your first show is also a good time to begin training your sheep for the showring if you have not yet begun. The amount of time that you spend training your animals will directly affect how well they will do. It will require many hours of patience and practice to perfect the skills you and your sheep will need in the showring.

Allow enough time to make, order, or purchase equipment and supplies that you will need to get your animals ready for the show. Also, make a list of supplies and equipment that you will need while at the show.

Mark the date for the last shearing of your market lambs. Put down when you should begin washing and fitting out your animals for the show.

Mark all dates for continuing and final preventive health care of your animals. Allow time to make a medical kit. Collect together any medications that you might possibly need while traveling or while you are at a show.

TRAINING FOR THE SHOWRING

WHERE TO LEARN ABOUT SHOWING

No one is born with the talent and ability needed to show sheep. To learn the correct ways of showing sheep, visit shows and watch those who are experienced showing sheep. Study how they handle their sheep in the showring. After attending some shows, you will be ready to develop and perfect the skills you saw demonstrated.

SHEEP IN THE SHOWRING

All of us have a problem remembering everything we have seen demonstrated. Read as much as you can about showing and look at as many pictures as possible showing the correct positions used in the showring.

Practicing the knowledge and training you have learned will make you and your animals more comfortable and confident when you are in the showring. The more you work at learning and practicing showing skills, the more skilled you will be at showing.

Even sheep who have been fed and finished properly may not win if they haven't been taught to lead well, stand calmly, set-up, and brace. Sheep can't learn these

121

things overnight and they can't learn them without you and practice - practice - practice!

MAKING A HALTER

To teach sheep to show, it must first learn how to be led. This will require that you purchase or make a halter that will not detract from your sheep's appearance. White-faced sheep look best in white halters and dark-faced sheep look best in black halters.

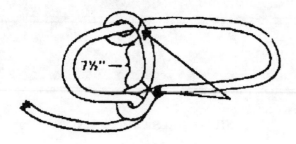

ROPE HALTER

An attractive low-cost halter can be made from 3/8 inch nylon rope. A 7 foot length of rope is enough to make one halter.

1. -- Cut the rope to the proper length.

2. -- After cutting the rope, have an adult seal each end of the rope by holding it over a flame until it melts slightly.

3. -- To make the halter, follow the illustration to loop the rope together.

The small loop goes under the chin; the large loop goes behind the ears and over the top of the head.

HALTER BREAKING

Before you can train your sheep to perform correctly in the showring, it should be halter broke. This is true whether you plan to show your animal with a halter or not. Halter-broke sheep are easier to handle and train to lead.

The halter used for your sheep should be adjustable so that it fits all weights and sizes of animals. The lead line should not be so long that the animal gets tangled in it.

Begin the training period about 8 weeks before the first show. It is usually necessary to tie the animal to a fence for short periods of time to help break it to a halter.

For a few days, tie the animal's lead line to the fence for about 15 minutes. Be sure the lead line is tied close enough to the fence that the animal is unable to tangle itself up in the line. **Do Not Leave The Animal Alone!** Sheep have been known to get entangled in the line.

At first, your sheep will probably fight the halter and being tied up. After a short time, it will realize that it can't get loose and will settle down. Once it has learned to stand tied to the fence without fighting, you are ready to teach it to lead.

TEACHING SHEEP TO LEAD

You will need to be very patient with your sheep at first in order to teach it to lead. You should be on the sheep's left side. Put a halter on it so that you can control it while you walk with it.

Sheep, especially lambs who are not used to being led, lead better if there isn't too much length left in the lead line. Leave about 12 inches to 18 inches of lead line between you and your animal.

Fold up the extra length of lead line and hold it in your hand. Walk slowly with the animal.

Your sheep will probably jump and pull against you. Be firm but patient with the animal. When it decides to jump or tries to run, stop and hold tightly to the lead line until it stops misbehaving. After it settles down, continue walking.

If the sheep will not move, hold the lead line in your left hand and tickle it under the dock (tail) with your right hand.

At first, you should practice leading and walking your sheep for only about 15 minutes. Once your sheep becomes used to being led, you can walk and exercise it for longer periods of time.

TEACHING SHEEP TO BE CALM

Now that your animal stands and walks well while being led, it must now learn not to be afraid of sounds.

Sometimes sheep will be frightened by a sound it isn't used to hearing. This can be a problem if this should happen while it is in the showring.

Get your sheep used to different sounds. Turn a radio on in the barn. Play different kinds of music. Play it loud and soft. Beat on a pan, blow a whistle, or toot a horn.

Next, it is important for you to get your sheep used to standing and leading even when it hears a loud or unusual sound.

While walking your sheep, have someone follow behind you. Have them clap their hands, make noises, and yell to get the sheep used to different sounds. Keep control of your sheep. Don't let it bolt or run away with you.

When your animal behaves well, praise it and give it a little treat. Some sheep enjoy treats such as miniature marshmallows, a few peanuts, or a small piece of apple. This is a reward that your sheep soon learn it should get when it does something right.

POSITIONS FOR SHOWING

Now that your sheep has calmed down and no longer fights the halter, you and your animal are ready to learn the basic positions used in the showring. Some of these positions will be more difficult for you or your animal to learn than others.

Remember that the more you practice the better you will become. While learning and practicing with your sheep, move slowly so as not to frighten it and always be gentle and patient.

HOW TO HOLD

Learn to hold your sheep correctly while it is wearing a halter so that you have control of it at all times before attempting to hold it without a halter. Cradle the sheep's lower jaw in your left hand with your thumb on one side and your fingers on the other.

CORRECT HOLDING OF SHEEP FOR SHOWING

Let go of the lead line and place your right hand across the back of the sheep's head just behind its ears with your thumb behind one ear and your fingers behind the other. This allows more control and keeps the ears pointed forward in a more alert position.

HEAD PLACEMENT

It is very important to know what is considered a proper head placement position. Holding your sheep's head in a proper natural position, along with correct placing of its legs, helps keep the animal's back straight and level.

The animal's head should be held in a natural position so that its nose is almost level with its back. A natural head position gives the sheep an active, alert appearance. Frequently beginners concentrate so hard on setting their animal's feet that they forget to keep the sheep's head at a correct angle.

PROPER HEAD PLACEMENT

Sheep who are allowed to let their neck, head, and nose droop to about a 180 degree angle to their body, a position that is almost level with their back, do not look as alert or appealing to the judge.

127

A mistake seen quite often is a sheep with its head held so high or upright that its nose is pointed skyward. Its nose, head, and neck make almost a 90 degree angle to its body. This can cause the animal's back to sag. Making it look as if it is weak across the back.

STOP-LEAD POSITION

You are now ready to learn the basic stop position. This is done while leading your sheep. You should already be on the sheep's left side. When using a halter, drop the lead line. Stop and gently put your right hand on the right side of the lamb's head and the left hand on the left side of its head.

Extend the fingers of your left hand down and curl them into the indentation under the bottom of the jawbone with your thumb extending up alongside the face between the eye and the ear. Move your right hand across the back of the sheep's head just behind its ears with your thumb behind one ear and your fingers behind the other and keep the sheep's ears pointing forward in an alert position.

It is better to stay on the left side to exhibit your sheep unless your show calls for you to switch as the judge moves past.

STOP-FRONT POSITION

The stop-front position is done in the stop position by moving around in front of your sheep and facing it. Place your right hand on the left side of the animal's head and your left hand on the right. Your fingers can be placed on either side of the sheep's neck behind the jaw line or along the animal's lower jaw. Your thumbs should lie along each side of the sheep's face parallel to and under its ears.

STOP-FRONT POSITION

Next, while holding onto its head, place your foot between its front legs with your knee resting against the brisket area but don't apply pressure. In this position, you are ready for the judge to handle your sheep.

GO-FORWARD POSITION

Once you are able to do the stop positions well, you are ready to learn how to move your sheep forward. While exhibiting your sheep in the showring, the judge may ask you to move your sheep from one place to another. Sheep are moved clockwise in the showring unless instructed by the judge otherwise.

MOVING SHEEP -- Start with the stop-lead position. The following two methods can be used with or without a halter but are more commonly used when the animal doesn't wear a halter.

GO-FORWARD HOLDING HEAD

Head Held Method -- Gently place your left hand under the sheep's jaw. Curl your fingers under and into the jaw indentation. Put your right hand behind its ears with your thumb behind one ear and your fingers behind the other.

Move the sheep by pushing it forward with your right hand. This method works well with sheep that don't like to be touched around their dock or tail.

GO FORWARD HOLDING HEAD AND DOCK

Head And Dock Holding Method -- If your sheep will not move by using the above method, it may be necessary for you to take your right hand from behind the ears and put it on the dock. Holding onto the dock, curl your fingers under it and pull up and forward gently.

This often causes the sheep to jump forward. Be prepared so that it doesn't get away from you. If this should happen, start over until you learn to control the sheep even if it should leap forward.

Halter Holding Method -- Most shows allow sheep to be shown with a halter. Young exhibitors often feel more in control of their sheep and more comfortable using a halter to move or walk their sheep in the showring. Keep the sheep's head up in a natural position while leading it.

This method of moving sheep is the least desirable because some animals may become stubborn and refuse to move. It is best to know the other two methods of moving sheep in case this happens.

SIDE VIEW LEG STANCE
Proper -- Sheep who are correctly posed will stand with their front and rear legs naturally under the four corners of their body. This is a natural, comfortable position for the sheep. Sheep are uncomfortable when their legs are placed in an awkward or unnatural position and wont stand still.

PROPER

133

Over-stretched -- A sheep who has been set up in an "over-stretched" pose has its front legs too far forward and its rear legs stretched too far back. This may cause its back to slump or sag, giving it an appearance of being swayback.

"OVER-STRETCHED"

Under-stretched -- When the front and rear legs of a sheep are placed too far under its body, it is under-stretched, causing the animal's back to hump-up or bow.

"UNDER-STRETCHED"

FRONT VIEW LEG STANCE

Proper -- Again, the front legs should be placed out at the corners of the sheep's body so that it stands naturally and comfortably.

PROPER

135

TOO NARROW

Too Narrow -- Whenever the sheep's front legs are placed too close together, it has the appearance of being too narrow through the chest.

Too Wide -- It makes sheep uncomfortable to stand with their front legs set too wide apart. Setting the front legs too wide apart gives the animal an unnatural appearance.

TOO WIDE

REAR VIEW LEG STANCE

Proper -- When viewing the sheep from the rear, its rear legs should be set squarely under its body in a comfortable, natural pose. This will show the natural muscling in the rear legs to its best advantage.

137

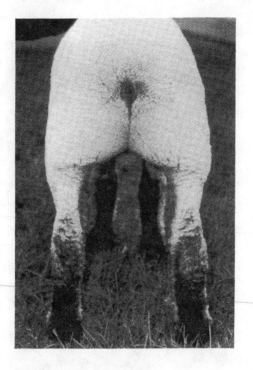

PROPER

Too Close Together -- Whenever a sheep's rear legs are placed too close together, it looks awkward. Close placement of the legs also makes the animal look as if it lacks muscling in the rear legs.

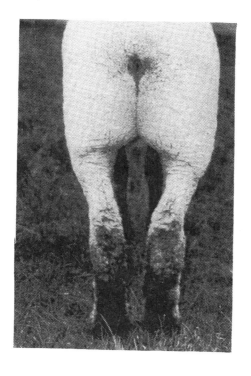

TOO CLOSE TOGETHER

Too Far Apart -- Sheep who have their rear legs spread too far apart are uncomfortable and because of this they often will not remain standing in this position.

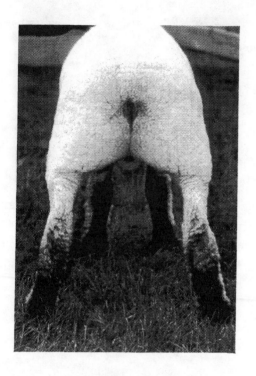

TOO FAR APART

LEG-SETTING

Sheep usually have a level back when they stand with their head and all four legs placed in a correct position. Before you can learn how to set a sheep's legs correctly, you must be able to tell when they have been set incorrectly. Study the pictures and descriptions, and practice setting your sheep up in the correct manner.

If you are a beginner, we usually recommend that you first learn how to set your sheep's legs while the animal is on a grooming stand. This lets you work with the sheep's head held in a natural position and allows you to learn where the legs should be when they are correctly placed under the animal.

For the sheep's feet to be correctly placed, they should be set squarely on the corners of its body. See the illustrations for proper leg stances.

Sheep do not like to have anyone catch or hold onto their legs. They often kick or try to get away if you try to pick up their leg by taking hold of the leg anywhere below the knee or hock. They are more cooperative if you pick the leg up just above these areas.

Once your sheep gets used to you picking up its legs and placing them in position while on the grooming stand, you can do the same thing from the squatting or standing position without use of the grooming stand.

Reaching Under -- While in the squatting position, use your right hand to reach underneath the sheep's belly and pick up the sheep's front leg that is closest to the judge, just above the knee, and set it down.

Repeat this with the rear leg that would be closest to the judge by picking the leg up in the area above the hock and moving it into position. Now set the legs on the side nearest you.

Reaching Over -- If you are tall enough, you can place or set the front leg that will be closest to the judge by reaching over the shoulder of your sheep while standing. Be sure to use the area above the sheep's knee for moving this leg into position.

Place the rear leg on the judge's side by reaching over the sheep's back and use the area just above the hock to set this leg. You can now squat down and place the legs on the side closest to you.

It is very important to be patient and yet firm with the sheep while teaching it to stand properly with its legs correctly placed. Once the sheep is standing correctly, check to make sure its head is in a natural position and its back is level.

Spend about 15 minutes each day practicing the leg-setting skills. It may take several weeks of practice before your animal learns to stand with its legs squarely underneath it.

TIGHTENING MUSCLES AND BRACING

There is a time while exhibiting sheep in the showring that the judge will wish to handle your animal. You should be ready to move around to the stop-front position when this occurs.

Judges handle sheep to determine how fat they are and to compare the loin, rump, and muscling of your sheep to others in the class.

Being able to make your sheep tighten its back and leg muscles while the judge is handling it is very important. If done correctly, it makes your sheep feel firmer to the judge's touch.

There are several ways to brace a sheep or cause it to tighten its muscles. Sometimes, two of these are used together. Never let anyone convince you that one of these ways is by lifting your sheep's front feet off the ground. This method causes the animal's muscles to feel soft, not firm.

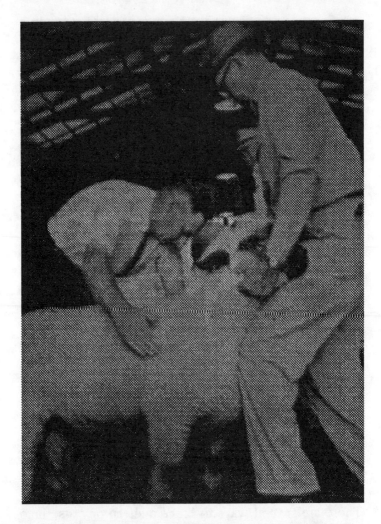

TIGHTENING AND BRACING POSITIONS

One way to cause a sheep to tighten its muscles is by putting pressure on its nose and face to force its head slightly downward so that it is looking toward the ground.

At the same time that you are pressing its head down, you should push against its head. This causes the animal's neck to bow slightly and it will push back against your pressure. When the sheep pushes back against your force, it tightens its leg and back muscles.

Another way is to place your hands on either side of the animal's neck and push against the muscles that run along the neck. The pressure placed against these muscles causes the sheep to lean towards you. This results in the back and leg muscles expanding so that they feel firm and hard when the judge handles the animal.

A third method for causing a sheep to tighten its muscles is called bracing. It is used more often by taller exhibitors. To brace your sheep, move around to the stop-front position.

Your fingers can either be placed alongside the animal's lower jaw neckline or on either side of the sheep's neck. Your thumbs should lie along each side of its face parallel to and under its ears.

Put one of your knees firmly against the animal's brisket and put pressure against the brisket to try to push it backward. This pushing against the brisket causes your sheep to push forward and tighten its back and leg muscles.

For your sheep to be able to push back when it is pushed against, it is important to set its rear legs in such a way that it can do this. If the rear legs are not set up squarely and instead are set too far apart or too close together, the sheep can't push back in a manner that would cause its muscles to tighten and be firm.

It is important to practice one of these methods often so that you are able to do it easily in the showring.

Correct tightening and bracing extend the back muscles to their full length and make them feel firmer. Practice - practice - practice this position. Many a sheep has lost out on first place because its handler braced it poorly.

EXHIBITOR STANCES

There are those who like to learn and practice the exhibitor stances and how to set legs without a halter. Since some shows require that sheep are shown in halter it is best to first learn how to set the animal's legs while wearing a halter before practicing the stances without a halter. I also think it is easier to learn these positions with a halter on the sheep because you have more control over the animal.

SQUATTING POSITION

Stand with your sheep in the go-forward position. Slowly move into a squatting position on the left side of your sheep. Hold the sheep's head at a natural angle.

Remove your hand from behind the animal's ears and carefully place it on its belly. If your sheep's back isn't level, push up slightly on the belly with this hand to make it level out its back and keep it straight.

Don't rub the belly of your sheep unless it is misbehaving. Too much stroking may cause a sheep to either arch its back or relax too much and look sloppy in the showring. If your animal arches its back, remove your hand from its belly and gently press down on the loin or arched area with your hand until it relaxes.

STANDING POSITION

A standing position is used more often by young beginners and small children to exhibit their sheep. By standing, they are able to keep better control of their sheep should the animal decide to jump or try to get away. Taller kids should try to learn and use the squatting position most of the time to exhibit their sheep because standing upright detracts from their sheep.

Practice these positions along with the other movements and positions you have learned until the sheep stands quietly. Once it remains calm and quiet, you are ready to learn how to set its legs.

PRACTICING WITHOUT A HALTER

You have now learned all the positions needed to show your sheep in the showring. It is time to practice all of the learned positions without a halter.

Practice in a small penned area so that it will be easier to catch your sheep should it get loose from you. If the sheep gets loose more than a couple of times, you need more practice with the halter still on the sheep. Above all, don't lose your temper with your sheep if it gets away from you. The sheep is only doing what sheep do whenever they are afraid.

WHEN TO PRACTICE

After you and your sheep learn all of the positions, you should spend time practicing. Each day walk, pose, set the sheep up, and brace it so that it doesn't forget what it has learned.

Make sure to practice each position correctly. Practice in front of your parents or a brother or sister. Ask them to let you know if you are doing each position correctly.

The amount of time you spend practicing with your sheep will directly affect your success in the showring.

SHOWMANSHIP

Most shows and fairs also hold showmanship classes for youth. Showmanship classes differ from judged sheep classes. A judged class primarily considers and places value on the sheep. A showmanship class also considers the skills of the exhibitor to show his/her sheep correctly.

You will be judged on your appearance and your sheep's appearance. You also will be judged on your ability to prepare or fit your sheep correctly for the showring. In showmanship classes, all sexes and breeds of sheep are eligible for showing.

If you decide to enter a showmanship class, there will be other skills and rules that you will need to know besides those learned for showing sheep in a judged market or breeding class.

Find out the rules and regulations of the show or fair for the showmanship classes you plan to enter because they may vary from show to show. Some shows require all animal to be shown with a halter while others require showing without a halter.

There are also differences among judges on showmanship styles. Find out what these differences are before the show if at all possible. The suggestions listed below also are important to follow for most showmanship classes.

Well-prepared Show Animal -- Find out the fitting requirements for the show and have your sheep clean, trimmed, and ready for the show in advance.

Suitable Dress -- Dress in a neat manner. I always told my kids that the way they looked reflected who they were. You and your clothes should be neat and clean.

Don't wear unsuitable clothes such as shorts, sleeveless tops, dresses, sandals, hats, or caps while showing. Leather boots or shoes look better in the showring and offer protection to your toes should a sheep step on your feet. Shoes should be clean and polished.

Your hair should be combed neatly. Long hair should be pulled back or braided so that it doesn't get in the eyes while trying to show sheep.

Never chew gum while in the showring. Don't kneel while in the showring because dirt or sawdust can get onto your knees and then get transferred to the sheep's wool.

Show Schedule -- Know the show schedule for the day that you show. Be prompt for your class. If after you arrive at the fairgrounds or show facility you don't know exactly when you will show, be ready well in advance and listen for the announcer to announce the class.

Right Attitude -- A right attitude is a proper way of conducting yourself. A good attitude, good manners, and good sportsman-like conduct are the result of a right attitude.

Maintain a good attitude even when you feel disappointed in the judge's decisions. Sometimes kids show a bad attitude when a judge places them in a lower position than what they feel they deserve. Some judges do this just to see if the exhibitor will continue to show a good attitude, before moving you back into a higher position.

Always show good manners in and out of the showring. Never crowd other exhibitors; this may cause them to lose control of their animal. Help fellow exhibitors in and out of the showring whenever possible.

Congratulate the winner after the show if you lose. If you are the winner, don't gloat. Be a gracious winner when someone congratulates you on winning, thank them for their words of congratulation.

Mistreating an animal before, during, or after showing is an example of poor sportsman-like conduct. Never beat, hit, slap, kick, or mistreat your sheep in any way. Your sheep will remember being mistreated by you and because it is afraid, it will not be cooperative.

Mistreating animals can produce enough stress to cause them to become sick later. Poor sportsman-like conduct also may cost you points if the judge sees you mishandling your sheep this way.

Maintain Eye Contact -- This really means knowing where the judge is at all times so that you can follow his directions promptly. Divide your attention between the judge and your sheep in order to make sure your animal remains correctly posed. Listen and follow instructions given to you by the judge or ring assistant.

Keep your attention focused on what is going on in the showring. Never talk or look at anyone in the audience.

Stay Calm -- Move smoothly and easily to position your sheep. Control your sheep at all times. Be patient and don't get discouraged if your sheep decides to be uncooperative.

If your sheep refuses to cooperate and remain in a correct position after a few attempts by you, let it be and don't become upset. Sheep sometimes have bad days just like people.

Overworking -- One problem often seen in the showring is the beginner who overworks his/her sheep. My definition of overworking is continuous handling of an animal. Usually the overworking is caused by repeated handling of the sheep's legs.

Another fault often seen in young exhibitors is constant scratching or rubbing of their sheep's belly. This should be avoided because too much stroking causes the sheep to either arch its back or relax too much and look sloppy.

THIRTY DAYS BEFORE THE SHOW

It is important to set aside enough time to get certain chores done before taking your sheep to the show. You should also leave time to get together all the equipment and supplies you may need while you are at the show.

Prepare a schedule of duties and list them on the last 30 days of your sixty day calendar.

DUTIES:
Entry Papers -- Be sure to get your entry papers to the proper authorities on time.

Preventive Health Care -- Make sure show sheep are up to date on their vaccinations and have been recently dewormed. Practice preventive stress management of all sheep being washed, fitted, or transported to the show. See below.

Medical Kit and Show Equipment -- Make a list of the items you will need for preparing your sheep for the show. Include those items needed while at the show.

Some items that should be listed include supplies for a medical supply kit and show box. Order or purchase the items early so that you have enough time to get everything collected together before it is needed. Some of these items may need to be ordered or purchased through your veterinarian.

Vet Health Care Visit -- Schedule a visit with your veterinarian for the show animals' health check. Do this early enough so that the health papers can be filled out and back in your hands in time for the show.

Shear Market Lambs -- Lambs should be shorn about two weeks before the show unless otherwise stated by specific rules of the show or fair.

Prepare Sheep For The Showring -- Set aside the last week to ten days before the show to get your sheep ready for the show. Pick a sunny day to wash your sheep so that they can dry more rapidly. They should be blanketed after washing and drying to keep them clean.

Trim and get your sheep totally ready for the show while they are still at home. Leave only last minute touching-up for a time after you arrive at the show.

PREVENTIVE HEALTH CARE
Do everything necessary to keep your show animals in good health. Make sure they are vaccinated and dewormed before traveling with them. Other medications, vitamins, and stress management skills are also beneficial for show animals. Follow the suggestions listed below.

14 Days Before Show -- Deworm your show animals if it has been more than two weeks since they were last dewormed. Use Safeguard cattle paste dewormer for this particular deworming because it causes less stress to the animal's system.

7 Days Before Show -- Give sheep the medications and vitamins listed below.

Start giving the sheep their daily water in a bucket if they haven't been getting it from one. Add buffered electrolytes to the water to disguise its flavor if you haven't already started doing so. Continue doing this while at the show. Use one of the products suggested under FEEDING FOR GREATEST GAIN -- WATER found elsewhere in the book.

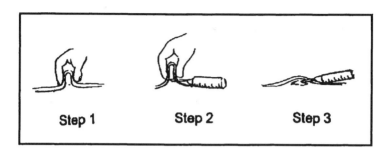

| Step 1 | Step 2 | Step 3 |

SUBCUTANEOUS INJECTION (Under the Skin)

Give show sheep 5cc/100 lbs of Vitamin B Complex subcutaneously each day that you must handle and work with them to prepare them for the show. All show lambs and sheep should also receive an injection of Vitamin B Complex before being transported to the show.

One week before the show, to help prevent pneumonia during this time and while being shown, give all animals IBR-PI3 intranasal vaccine even if they have been vaccinated earlier. They should be given 1/2 cc per nostril. This will provide some protection against pasteurella pneumonia which causes Shipping Fever Pneumonia.

To boost the animal's immune system, give it a subcutaneous injection of Vitamin A&D lambs - 1 cc, adult sheep - 2 cc. Each animal should also be given Vitamin E 600IU to 800IU/100lbs either the oral variety or a subcutaneous injection.

STRESS REDUCTION

Weather changes, hot weather, long hours being washed and prepared for the show, not eating or drinking on schedule, and traveling can all cause stress. Keep these stresses and other stress to your show animals at a minimum so that they will stay healthy.

1. -- Wash your sheep or lambs on a sunny day.

2. -- Shear and trim them early in the morning before the temperature becomes hot.

3. -- Don't keep your animals on the trimming stand for long periods of time. Plan your trimming so that it can be spaced out with a break for you and your lamb in between periods of trimming.

4. -- Feed your animals on schedule.

5. -- Plan to load and travel with your sheep to the show while the temperature is cooler. Try to have them unloaded before noon.

6. -- Allow your animals to rest after being moved; don't do any work on them that day.

MEDICAL SUPPLY KIT

The best way to safeguard your sheep during the show season is to go on the road with a prepared medical kit containing products and supplies that you may need in an emergency. It's important to keep these products with you whenever you travel.

The following is a list of supplies we included in our medical kit when we took sheep to shows and sales. The list looks extensive. However, many of these products were used to help other exhibitors save the life of one or more sheep at a show or fair.

MEDICAL KIT CONTENTS:

Alcohol -- Fill a small plastic bottle with alcohol to pack in your kit. The alcohol is used to disinfect needles and tops of bottles before giving an injection.

Antibiotic - Injectable -- Choose an injectable product that doesn't require refrigeration. We use Procaine Penicillin G, Spectam which contains spectinomycin, or BP-48 which is a long acting penicillin. These products can be used should an animal develop a cold or other bacterial infection.

Epinephrine -- This is just in case the animal has an allergic reaction to a shot. Give 1cc/100 lbs.

Antibiotic - Oral -- An oral antibiotic is sometimes needed to treat an animal with diarrhea. Spectam Scour Halt or Spectogard are liquid oral preparations used for this purpose. We start with one of these drugs at the first sign of diarrhea. We also carry a supply of Sulmet oblets and use these if one of the others doesn't work.

Anti-Diarrhea Mixture -- These products are used to relieve simple diarrhea and as supportive therapy in cases of bacterial scours or digestive upsets. We use maximum strength Pepto Bismol. Older lambs and

159

adult sheep need 30cc/100 lbs or more every 4 to 6 hours.

Aspirin -- Use aspirin to lower temperature of animals with a fever or to reduce pain.We use 1 adult aspirin per 40 pound's body weight every 6 hours.

Balling Gun -- This is needed for administering boluses, aspirin, ibuprofen, or other oral pills.

Bicarbonate of Soda -- Add a small box of Arm & Hammer Baking Soda to your supplies. Baking soda is useful for making a buffered water drench or drinking water solution. One teaspoon of soda can be added to 16 ounces of water to make a drench or two tablespoons into one gallon of water to make a buffered drinking water solution.

Choke Tube -- This is a home-made device used to relieve choking in sheep from an obstruction in their throat. Choking is usually caused by lodged grain or feed pellets. It's frequently needed for show sheep because they often are very aggressive eaters and bolt their food down.

To make a tube, cut off a 2-foot length of 3/8 or 1/2 inch garden hose and file the cut edges down smooth. If the tube is needed, pass it down the throat to dislodge whatever is obstructing the passage. It may be necessary to do this more than once.

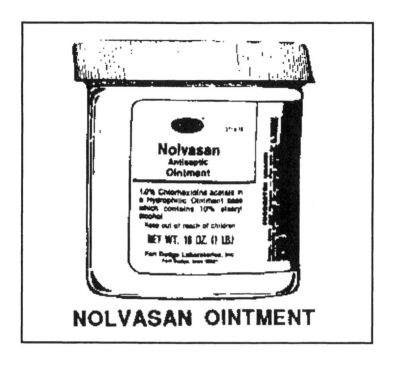

NOLVASAN OINTMENT

Chlorhexiderm Shampoo or Nolvasan Shampoo with Conditioner -- This shampoo is available in 8 oz. or gallon size. It is used on animals with skin conditions such as ringworm where an antiseptic, anti microbial, and cleansing formulation may be of benefit. The shampoo contains Chlorhexidine diacetate .5%.

Nolvasan Skin And Wound Cleanser - This product contains Chlorhexidine. It helps damaged tissue heal rapidly without causing irritation and is a gentle cleanser that helps prevent infection. According to the label, it is effective against bacteria, yeast, and fungus infections, including ringworm.

Cottonballs -- These are used, saturated with alcohol, to disinfect needles, etc.

Electrolyte Water Soluble Powder -- Electrolyte solutions are commonly used whenever a sheep isn't eating and as treatment for dehydration from diarrhea, fever or heatstress. We use electrolyte products with a buffering compound such as Renew by AgriLabs, Electrolytes Plus from Tri-Mutual Inc. and Bovine Bluelite available through Pipestone Veterinary Supply, 1-800-658-2523.

Fly Repellent -- This gives all show animals relief from biting flies. It should be put on the animal before it enters the showring to prevent flies from landing on the animal while it is being shown.

Iodine 7% -- This is useful to disinfect and dry wounds.

Milanta II -- This is an oral human antacid preparation. We give it to animals with bloat or acidosis at 60cc/100lbs once a day for two days.

Needles and Syringes (Disposable) -- Carry several 18 to 20 gauge needles and a few 3cc, 12cc, 20cc and one 60cc disposable syringes. The 60 cc syringe can be used to orally drench sheep. A 1/2 inch long needle is satisfactory for giving subcutaneous injections. Use a 3/4 to 1 inch needle for intramuscular injections.

Thermometer -- This is needed to check a sick animal's temperature. **Normal temperature is 102` F to 103` F.**

Udder Infusion Tube -- Keep an antibiotic mastitis udder infusion tube in the kit. It can be used as a substitute eye ointment or to treat wounds, especially puncture wounds.

Vitamin B Complex -- This vitamin helps protect the animal's brain and nervous system. It is needed for energy production and is a natural tranquilizer. It is given at the rate of 5cc/100lbs subcutaneously. It is given before transporting, fitting, showing or any time the animal is stressed or sick.

SHOW EQUIPMENT

LARGE EQUIPMENT:
Make a list of all the equipment you will need while at the show. Large equipment should include a portable box fan, heavy duty extension cord, farm sign, broom, straw or other bedding, water buckets and a feeder or feed pans.

Bring enough feed and hay for the entire stay at the show. You should also include a grooming stand and a bucket for soapy water if you plan to fit and trim your sheep out at the show.

SHOW BOX

Outfit a box or trunk with the tools and small items you may need to get ready for the show. You will take this box with you to all shows that you attend. This is also a good place to keep this book and your medical kit.

SHOW BOX EQUIPMENT:

Some items will be used at home to prepare your sheep for the show but can be stored in the box should you need them at the show.

Pack the following tools and equipment:

Flashlight	Soft-bristle brush
Hammer and nails	Metal curry comb
Length of rope for hanging a sign	Halter
Hoof shears	Wool cards
Washcloth	Electric shears
Towels	Hand shears

In addition:

Include liquid soap such as Ivory or Dove hand dishwashing liquid if you plan to wash animals at a show. If there has been any cases of club lamb fungus at your fairgrounds, you may want to use "Chlorhexiderm Shampoo". See Medical Supply Kit for a description of this cleaning liquid.

Don't forget to pack show blankets, hoods, large blanket pins, or a spandex lamb sweater if you plan to prepare your sheep at the show.

Also include a sewing needle, thread, scissors, and safety-type baby diaper pins. These come in handy for quick repairs or if you lose a button or get a tear in your clothing.

FITTING SHEEP FOR SHOWING

ADVANCED PREPARATIONS

Preparing animals for showing is commonly referred to as fitting.

A fitting job starts well in advance of the show. It begins shortly after you purchase your animals. Your sheep should already have been sheared one or more times depending on the class they will be in.

Now you are down to the last couple weeks before the show and the final preparations of your sheep for the show. You will need to trim their hooves, shear their belly (if they are breeding sheep), wash and ready them for the specific class they will be shown in.

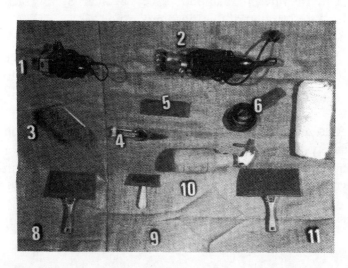

12) HAND SHEARS

FITTING EQUIPMENT
See picture above and on the previous page.
1)   Small animal clippers.
2)   Electric sheep shears.
3)   Clean brush.
4)   Hoof trimmer.
5)   Whet stone for sharpening hand shears.
6)   Curry comb.
7)   Clean towel or cloth.
8)   No. 2 card.
9)   No. 4 or 5 pocket card for head and legs.
10)   Spray bottle.
11)   No. 3 card.
12)   Hand shears shown separately.

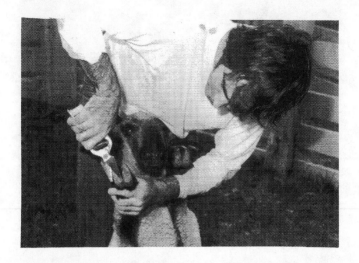

TRIMMING HOOVES

One of the first jobs in proper fitting is trimming your animal's hooves. This should be done several days before the show and before washing the animal if you plan to trim their hooves while they are sitting on their rump. You can trim hooves after the animal is washed while it is standing on the grooming stand. Follow the hoof trimming procedure you learned earlier in the book.

FITTING STYLES

There are several methods of preparing sheep for show. Most sheep being shown in a breeding class are fitted out differently than those in market lamb classes. Because of these differences, Each method used to fit out a sheep will be discussed separately.

168

There may be other differences in the way sheep are presented for the showring. Check the rules and regulations for your shows before fitting your sheep.

PREPARING BREEDING SHEEP
Sheep shown in breeding classes from the meat-breeds (Suffolks, Hampshires, Dorsets, etc.) are usually shown with fleece long enough that it can be carded and trimmed just before a show. The fleece length is usually no more than 1 inch over the major portion of the body. Leave the fleece slightly longer than 1 inch over the rump and upper leg.

If you plan to card and trim your breeding sheep, their last shearing should be about 80 to 90 days before the first show. The fleece is then allowed to grow out until fitting time.

BELLY SHEARING
The underside of the sheep's breast and belly and the inside of each rear leg should first be shorn to prepare it for washing, carding and trimming. Don't shear too far up from the belly on the sides of the animal.

If you have difficulties determining just where to shear, place the sheep on its rump and with a piece of colored chalk draw an oval to outline the area to be shorn.

Begin the oval at a point inside the right fore flank and draw a chalk line to a point inside the right rear flank.

Making a natural oval, extend and continue the chalk line over to a point inside the left rear flank, up to the inside left fore flank, then in an oval back over to the right fore flank.

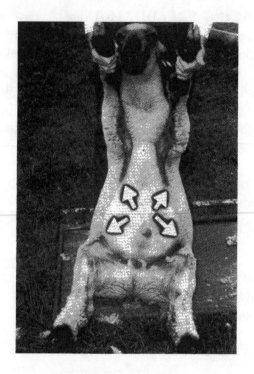

BELLY SHEARING

Be careful during the shearing process to avoid clipping the sheath of males or the teats of ewes.

The reasons for shearing the belly and inside rear legs of the sheep are that it makes them look trimmer through the middle and shows off their natural length. It shows the width through the rear legs when viewed from the rear. Shearing these areas also cuts down on the amount of hand trimming needed during the carding and trimming stage.

ROUGH BLOCKING

The first stage of the trimming process is known as "rough blocking". It is used for sheep who were not sheared within the past two months.

(1) -- Dampen the fleece all over with soapy water from a bucket by brushing it into the sheep's fleece. After it appears slightly crusty from the dampening, it is ready to be combed.

(2) -- Using the curry comb, comb the fleece forcefully all over.

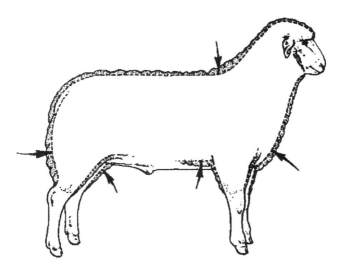

DETERMINING WHERE TO TRIM

(3) -- Before beginning the trimming process, it is important to look at your sheep and decide where and how much fleece to remove. See the *Illustration*.

Try to imagine how you can improve the overall appearance of the animal by removing a little fleece in certain areas. The objective at this time is to decide how much wool to trim from the back to make it level and from the center areas of the sides to develop a somewhat straighter side.

(4) -- Using the hand shears, trim the back level and trim off excess wool from the center of the sides. See THE CARDING AND TRIMMING PROCESS for directions on learning to use hand shears.

After you gain experience, you will be able to do the rough blocking with the electric shears.

(5) -- The animal can now be washed if the show date is within a week. If not, let the animal loose until you are ready to wash it.

SHOW BLANKETS

Show blankets and hoods are used to cover sheep whose fleece has been washed, carded, and trimmed for a show. Blanket sizes usually available include small, medium, large, and extra large. Small-sized blankets usually fit market lambs. The larger sizes are used for various sizes of breeding sheep.

The purpose of a blanket is to keep your animal clean. Hoods to keep the head clean are also available in various sizes. The hood is pinned at the blanket back. If hoods are used, be sure to check the animal's eyes daily because hoods sometimes irritate eyes and can cause turned-in eyelids.

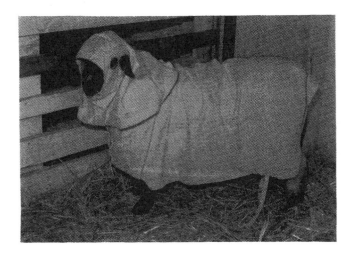

SHOW BLANKETS

The blanket should be left on the sheep at all times except when trimming, weighing in at the fair, and of course, showing. The body blanket is held on by two leg straps, one on each back leg.

Spandex lamb sweaters are commonly used on slick-sheared market lambs. They keep the lamb clean, smooth wrinkles, and keep pressure on the hide.

You can make very nice blankets for your sheep. The blankets can even be stenciled with your name, logo, or farm name on them.

WASHING

Market lambs shown slick shorn can be sheared and then washed if you so desire.

Sheep should be washed some time during the final week before the show. Choose a warm sunny day to wash them. If at all possible, use warm water for washing and rinsing the animals.

Collect everything together that you will need to wash your sheep. Try washing and rinsing them within a 15 minute time period. This helps keep stress to the animals at a minimum.

Place your animal on a grooming stand and secure its head in the head piece. Use a round curry comb and rake the fleece lightly to break up and remove dried dirt, burrs, straw, and other debris.

Wad together enough cotton balls to put into each of the animal's ears. Water that gets into the ear can sometimes cause an animal to hold its head in an odd position. If you choose not to put cotton balls in the ears, hold the ears down while washing and rinsing the sheep to avoid this problem. You are now ready to wash your sheep.

There are two methods of washing sheep for shows. One is with a water hose and the other is tub bathing.

Most people use the hose method because it is easier. However, care must be taken not to turn in the wool fibers. Once the fibers are turned in it is difficult to get a smooth carding job.

Fibers that are turned in are not a problem with tub washing.

HOSE WASHING

HOSE WASHING

Sheep are commonly washed with a hose while standing on a grooming stand with their head secured in the head piece. They can also be tied to a fence line to be washed.

Once a sheep is put on a grooming stand, don't leave it alone. Sometimes, sheep step off the stand. If this happens while the sheep is unattended, it may become injured.

Pre-rinsing -- The sheep is first pre-rinsed by using moderate water pressure from the hose. Keep the nozzle of the hose angled to avoid skin injury and the turning inward of fleece. This is especially important of lambs who have been slick shorn.

Thoroughly wet the fleece by gently running water all over the sheep's body. Warm water will penetrate the lanolin in the fleece and release more dirt than cold water.

Shampooing -- Use a liquid hand dishwashing soap such as Ivory or Dove. Soap the sheep's wet fleece down well by pouring some liquid soap into your hands, work up a good lather and work it into the animal's fleece.

Liquid soap applied to fleece directly from the bottle is too concentrated and will leave white lines in the fleece after it dries.

Do a thorough cleaning job. Pay special attention to the areas under the legs, the belly, the rear of ewes, and the testicles of rams. Do the sheep's head last and try not to get soap into its eyes.

Rinsing -- Carefully rinse all of the soap from the fleece using the same moderate water pressure and nozzle angle from the hose used for the pre-rinsing. It is important to get all of the soap rinsed out, otherwise it will irritate and dry out the sheep's skin.

If the animal has been slick shorn, skip the curry combing step and go directly to the drying step.

Curry Combing -- Excess water held in the fleece is now removed with a clean curry comb. Start at the top back part of the head and gently pull the rake straight down the neck to the backline.

CURRY COMBING

177

Continue raking the rest of the neck and chest fleece in a straight down manner. Next, rake in a straight line from the base of the neck back to the dock. The fleece on the sides and rear is pulled straight down.

You should also curry the belly. This should be done gently and very carefully because of the exposed skin in this area. Continue currying the lamb in this pattern until you have removed as much water as possible.

Drying -- Halter and tie the washed and curried sheep to a fence line to dry before covering them with a body blanket. Choose an area where the grass is clean just in case the animal tries to lie down or fights being tied and falls down.

Some people use a blow-dryer or hair dryer to dry their animals. There are disadvantages to this method. Blow dryers turn in the fibers and make the fleece more difficult to card out. Frequent use of a dryer causes the fleece to appear dead or dull.

Blanketing -- Cover the sheep with a sheep body blanket and hood in the appropriate size.

Sheep who are going to be carded and fitted should be almost dry before they are covered with a sheep blanket to keep them clean. However, covering a slightly damp animal improves the packing ability of the wool.

Place your animal in a clean pen that has been well bedded with straw or wood shavings. Be sure that any surface the animal might come in contact with is also clean.

Allow at least 24 hours to pass before carding and trimming the freshly washed animal. This lets some of the natural lanolin return to the wool and makes it easier to card and trim.

TUB WASHING

Kevin Kuykendall taught us the tub method of washing sheep. He showed our purebred sheep in competition for many years.

Kevin and his wife Sarah are expert fitters and showmen. They are very well known in purebred circles for their abilities. They make an animal look and show to its greatest advantage. I can't praise this couple enough and highly recommend them to anyone who needs an animal fitted for a show or sale.

While Kevin showed for us, he was always very helpful to people new to showing, especially young people. If you ever attend a show or sale where Kevin and Sarah are fitting out sheep, spend some time observing them.

Few people who have spent time watching the Kuykendalls fit out an animal have come away from the experience without a better understanding of fitting.

With the tub washing method, the dirt is loosened by soaping, soaking, and then floating the dirt out of the wool fibers. This prevents turned in fibers that are difficult to straighten, as usually happens with the hose washing method.

The process of tub washing requires two people unless you are an expert at it. Expect to get wet. We always did. Sometimes I felt I was as wet as the sheep and should have been tied alongside them on the fence line to dry. It does feel good though on a hot summer day!

Two or three stock watering tanks are used to bathe and rinse the sheep. The tanks are lined up side by side, parallel and adjacent to each other and filled with lukewarm water. If you can't provide warm water, fill the tubs with water the day before washing. This allows the water to absorb the heat from the sun, making it warm enough to use for washing on the following day.

Tub Washing Instructions:

(1) -- Put a halter on the sheep.

(2) -- Position the sheep parallel to the 1st filled wash tub.

To flip the sheep into the tub, place your hand under its jaw, turn its head up and away from the tub as you flip it into the tub and onto its back, keeping its head above water.

A second person may be needed to help flip the animal into the tub. Ease the sheep into the tub and release its feet.

(3) -- Once the sheep has been thoroughly wetted down, allow it to stand up.

(4) -- Using a mild liquid hand dishwashing detergent such as Ivory or Dove, pour some soap into your hands, work up a lather, and rub it into the animal's fleece. A soft bristled brush can be used to scrub the animal if you wish. Pay special attention to the belly and under the legs. Finally, wash the head.

(5) -- After completing the soaping and scrubbing, use a curry comb to help break apart and loosen any stubborn dirt caught in the fleece.

(6) -- Flip the animal back onto its back into the water, while holding its head above the water, to remove the loosened dirt and soap. Afterward, allow the animal to stand.

(7) -- To rinse the remainder of the soap from the sheep's wool, flip the sheep from the soapy washing tank into the 1st rinse tank. Lift the sheep up and down and slosh it around.

To rinse the soap from the animal's head, pinch its nose closed with your fingers and quickly lower it into the water until the water is over its head. Release the animal and allow it to stand up as soon as possible.

(8) -- If the sheep was very dirty and/or extra soapy it may be necessary to give it a 2nd or final rinse in a 3rd tank.

(9) -- After all soap has been rinsed from the sheep, carefully remove the animal from the rinse tank. Lead it with the halter to a fence line or other area where there is clean grass or straw and tie it up.

Remove excess water with a curry comb, unless the animal has been slick shorn, and allow it to dry.

Show animals that will be carded and trimmed later should be left tied until they are fairly dry. Sheep dry quite rapidly on warm sunny days. Cover the animal with a clean show blanket and hood.

Place the sheep in a clean pen that has been bedded thickly with fresh straw or wood shavings.

Allow the animal to remain blanketed in the pen for at least 24 hours. This amount of time gives the lanolin a chance to return to the wool.

Lanolin helps "set" the fleece before carding and trimming begins. Trimming the fleece while it is still soft and before it is set often leaves shear marks in the fleece.

As noted before, covering a slightly damp animal helps the wool pack better.

LAMB ON A GROOMING STAND

PREPARING MARKET LAMBS

WASHING
Wash your market lambs at home about 3 days before the show. Either method used for washing breeding sheep described earlier can be used to wash market lambs. Follow the directions outlined for the particular method.

SHEARING
Most fairs require that lambs shown in market classes be shorn to the skin. Sometimes the difference between

first and second place is no more than how smooth the shearing job is between the two lambs.

In some market lamb shows the lambs are "poodle clipped", leaving about 1 inch of wool on the hips, rump, and dock. Poodle clipping is described later.

Slick shear about two weeks before a show with a 20-toothed goat comb. If using a comb other than a goat comb, be careful to avoid shear cuts and be sure the animal is shorn smoothly.

SLICK SHEARING

SLICK SHEARING
The 20-tooth goat comb is used to slick shear market lambs. Make sure that all parts of the lamb are sheared completely and left very smooth.

SHEARING SEQUENCE:

(1) -- Place the lamb on a grooming stand. Secure its head in a natural position.

(2) -- First, shear the lamb's underbelly and the inside of its legs.

(3) -- Next, shear the back, beginning at the dock and continuing to the base of the neck. Make sure to use long shearing strokes. Each shearing stroke along the back thereafter is in the same direction as the first and should be straight and parallel to the first stroke.

(4) -- The sheep's sides are sheared in the same direction as the back, from the rear of the animal to the front. Pull the skin tight with your left hand as you shear with your right hand to get the smoothest possible shearing job. Reverse this if you are left-handed.

Keep your strokes straight and level. A sheep's natural body length is improved upon by keeping the shearing strokes straight and parallel to each other.

(5) -- Next, the front and rear legs from the knee up are sheared in upward strokes. This helps prevent injuries to the legs. Animals with excessive amounts of lower leg wool may need the lower legs clipped as well.

(6) -- Finally, beginning at the point of the shoulder, shear forward and upward toward the head. Following the same upward strokes, shear the brisket and neck. This will show the animal's natural long neck to its best advantage.

(7) -- Cover the lamb with a spandex lamb sweater or show blanket and hood, described earlier, before removing it from the grooming stand. Lambs that have been completely slick sheared will remain covered until the preshow touch-up.

The Spandex sweater works well on slick-sheared market lambs. It keeps the lamb clean and prevents and smoothes skin wrinkles by keeping pressure on the hide.

(8) -- Place the animal in a clean pen that is thickly bedded with fresh straw or wood shavings to keep it clean until it is transported to the show. Add fresh bedding each day to the pen so that the animal stays clean.

POODLE CUT - LEAVING BREECHES OR PANTS

Some shows allow wool to be left over the rump. After the first shearing, lambs are sheared from the rear flanks forward each month beginning about 2 months before show time. They are not sheared over the hips, rump, and dock during this time. The wool that is left on the rear of the lamb is blended in later.

The mistake most beginners make is not carding enough to get a full firmly packed wool throughout the rump and upper leg. The purpose of fitting a lamb out in this manner is to enhance the muscling throughout these areas. It should show off the lamb's length of body, balance, and full leg muscling.

If you are not experienced at Poodle cutting, it might be better not to attempt it until you have practiced it a few times.

POODLE CUT SEQUENCE:
(1) -- Follow Step 1 and Step 2 in the directions given above for SLICK SHEARING.

(2) -- Begin shearing down the back from a point located in front of the hip bone to the base of the neck. Using this point as a guide, make parallel shearing strokes in the same direction as the first stroke.

(3) -- Follow Step 4 through Step 6 listed above for SLICK SHEARING, leaving the wool untouched from the rear flanks backward.

(4) -- Cover the lamb with a show blanket and hood before removing it from the grooming stand. Do not use a Spandex sweater on a Poodle clipped lamb.

Place the lamb in a clean pen that has been bedded well with clean straw or wood shavings for about 24 hours to let the wool over the rear of the lamb dry.

(5) -- On the next day, put the lamb back on the grooming stand so that you can card and trim the wool over the rump and rear legs.

(6) -- Follow the directions given for dampening fleece and carding that are outlined for breeding sheep.

(7) -- You are now ready to shape the fleece over the rump. Trim the top straight and nearly level from the area of the back that is slick sheared to the area back over the dock. Next trim out over the hips and taper this area into the slick sheared sides.

(8) -- To shape the rear legs and lower back area of the rump, continue trimming the lower portion of the rump, rounding and blending or tapering it to between the rear legs. There should be a visual separation between the two legs. The fleece on the leg that is above the hock is cut closer and blended or tapered to the leg.

(9) -- After the trimming is finished, spray a mist of soapy-water solution over the carded and trimmed fleece. Use the flat back of your card and pat the carded wool all over. This smoothes and helps hold the fleece in place, giving it a packed, compact appearance and feel.

(10) -- Re-cover the lamb with its blanket and hood and place it in a pen with fresh clean bedding until it is transported to the show. Add fresh bedding each day to the pen so that the animal stays clean.

THE CARDING/TRIMMING PROCESS

We use a three-stage process to card and trim our sheep once they have been washed and allowed to dry. These stages include the initial trimming, final trimming and preshow touch-up. Each of these stages is carried out with the animal on the grooming stand.

The initial and final trimming is covered in this section. The preshow touch-up is covered later in the TRAVELING AND CARE AT THE SHOW section.

Make sure that you have all the tools you will be using collected close at hand before placing your animal on the grooming stand. **Do not leave an animal alone on a grooming stand.** Animals can step off a stand and injure themselves in a matter of seconds.

Add about one tablespoon of liquid soap to a bucket of water and fill a spray bottle with some of the soapy water. Keep your sheep shears in the remainder of the soapy water in the bucket to keep them lubricated while trimming.

HOW TO USE TRIMMING SHEARS

The most popular hand shears recommended for the beginner is straight-edge rigged shears. They have a leather hand strap making it easier to maintain a good grip. It is a good idea to have a leather shear holder to protect the blades. Most hand shears are made for right-handed people.

Hold the shears in your right hand. The bottom blade of the shears is kept still and next to the fleece while the top blade is opened and closed by your four fingers to complete each cut. Move the shears in a straight line.

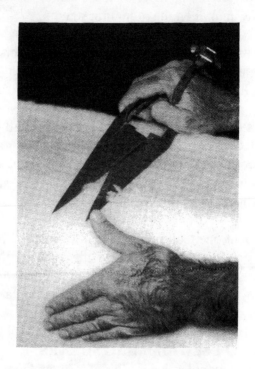

HOW TO USE TRIMMING SHEARS

Once a cut in the fleece has been made with the upper blade, slide the bottom blade slowly away from you to the edge of the smooth just clipped spot and take another cut.

Hold the shears at a right angle to the line of trimming. Take small cuts of wool and continue slowly to produce a smooth appearance. You can always take more wool off if necessary but you can't put it back on!

HOW TO CARD

The No. 2 card is used for light, open fleece and by some for the second carding and trimming. The No. 3 card, for heavy, dense fleece, is the most commonly used card. The No. 4 and No. 5 cards are used around the head, ears, and legs, and for general touch-up work.

The purpose of carding sheep is to straighten the wool fibers. When the fibers are straightened, they can then be cut off evenly. This gives the animal a smoother, more desirable appearance.

You can never card a sheep too much before a show. The more you do it, the better the sheep look. However, you will have to trim after each carding.

I like to compare a well-carded sheep's fibers to a thick plush-pile carpet. Expensive thick plush-pile carpets spring back after being walked upon, an inexpensive carpet will not. This is because there are more straight fibers per square inch lending support to each other in an expensive carpet compared to an inexpensive one.

When each fiber is straightened to stand upright, it then supports the straightened fiber next to it. If each and every fiber isn't straightened, there will be gaps in the finished product.

These gaps may be so tiny that they are not visible but they can account for the difference between the thick springy feel of a well-carded sheep and the loose, easily disturbed, fleece of a poorly carded sheep. The fibers of a well-carded sheep, like an expensive plush-pile carpet, will stand straight and be compact for many months after a show.

Before you begin carding your sheep, feel the sharp teeth of the card. Lightly strike your finger with the card's teeth. It is very painful. Be aware of how this would feel to your animal should the card's teeth touch its skin.

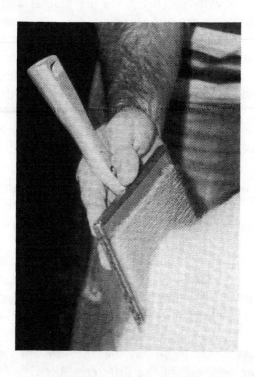

HOW TO HOLD A SHEEP CARD

Hold the card tightly in your hand and put the whole of the card's teeth in the sheep's fleece. Give the card a slight forward pull to insert the teeth in the fibers. Now lift it up in a revolving motion to separate the fibers. The motion used is a back-handed motion with the teeth of the card down so that they hook into the wool.

Pull the card from the fleece with either a wrist or fore-arm movement.

When you card, make sure that you use all the teeth on the card's face or you will create a rippled or ridging effect. Should this happen, it is almost impossible to get a smooth trimming job. Remove wool frequently from your card with a card cleaner or a table fork to keep all of the teeth exposed.

When competition to be the winner is stiff, you must card, re-card, and card some more to capture first place.

Never stick your fingers down into the fleece of a carded and trimmed animal ready to be shown. This bends fibers over and leaves holes in the fleece.

INITIAL CARDING AND TRIMMING
The initial trimming is more complete than the rough blocking described earlier.

(1) -- After the animal is placed on the grooming stand, remove the head cover and blanket from the animal.

(2) -- If the sheep's feet were not trimmed before it was washed, do this now.

193

(3) -- Dampen the sheep's fleece with a little of the soapy water from the bucket. The soapy water helps soften the fleece and makes it easier to card. It can be applied by either brushing it onto the fleece or rubbing it into the fleece with a clean washcloth or small towel.

Don't get the fleece too wet. You can add more moisture to the fleece if you need it during the trimming process by misting the fleece with the soapy-water from the spray bottle.

Fig. 1

(4) -- Beginners should card the sheep all over before doing any trimming (see Fig. 1). Begin at the top of the sheep. Start with the back and then the sides, shoulder, and front upper leg, Next do the rear of the animal and finish by doing the breast and neck.

Fig.2

(5) -- You are now ready to trim. Begin with the top (see Fig. 2). You can either trim from the neck to the dock or from the dock to the neck depending upon which is the easiest for you. The purpose is to make the back smooth and level.

195

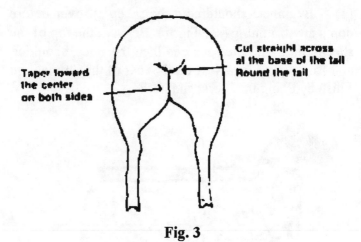

Taper toward
the center
on both sides

Cut straight across
at the base of the tail
Round the tail

Fig. 3

(6) -- The fleece at the rear (see Fig. 3) is trimmed so that it is rounded over the rump to the dock and down each side to blend with the inside of the rear legs.

Don't leave too much fleece on the top and sides of the rump. The widest portion of the animal should be through the stifle region.

(7) -- Trim the outward side of the rear legs (see Fig. 4) to blend with each side and over the rump.

(8) -- To shape the rear legs and lower back area of the rump, continue trimming the lower portion of the rump. Round and blend or taper it down to between the rear legs.

There should be a visual separation between the two legs. The fleece on the leg that is above the hock is cut

196

closer and blended or tapered to the leg to best show the muscling.

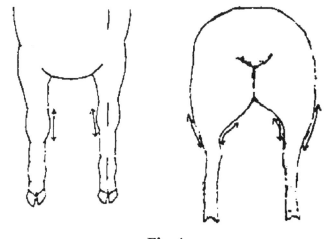

Fig. 4

(9) -- Next, trim the sides smooth and blend it into the top and the contour of the forelegs.

(10) -- Taper the fleece at the bottom edge of the sides into the slick sheared underbelly. You shouldn't be able to see where the slick shearing ended and the trimmed longer fleece begins.

Extra carding may be necessary in this area to get it well-tapered and smooth. My daughter found that the small No. 4 or No. 5 pocket card worked well in this area.

(11) -- Finally, trim the neck, chest, and front legs, blending them into the underbelly, shoulders, and back.

197

(12) -- Cover the animal again with its coat and hood and put it back into a clean pen with fresh bedding until you are ready to give it the final trimming.

FINAL TRIMMING

You are now ready for the final trimming.

(1) -- Remove the hood and coat.

(2) -- Dampen, card, and trim the sheep in the same sequence used for the initial trimming.

(3) -- After you are satisfied that the sheep has been trimmed well enough, spray a mist of soapy-water solution over the fleece. Using the flat back of your card, pat the carded wool all over. This smoothes and helps hold the fleece in place, giving it a packed, compact appearance and feel.

(4) -- Cover the animal again with its coat and hood and place it back into a clean pen bedded with fresh straw or wood shavings until time to transport it to the show. Add new bedding each day to the pen so that the animal stays clean.

TRAVELING AND CARE AT THE SHOW

LOADING

The night before traveling to the show, load everything that you plan to take to the show. By doing this before the sheep are loaded, you will reduce the amount of time needed before you can travel with your animals. Being prepared to travel as soon as the sheep are loaded will help reduce stress on your sheep.

Review and follow the other suggestions outlined earlier in the book for transport care.

Sheep travel better on less than a full stomach. Sheep transported before or close to their normal morning feeding period can be given a little hay after arriving at the show to carry them over until their next normal feeding time.

Give sheep only half their normal amount of feed if they are going to travel within a few hours of their normal morning feeding time.

Before placing your sheep on the truck or trailer and transporting them to the show, make sure to give each animal a subcutaneous injection of Vitamin B Complex 5cc/100lbs. This vitamin helps reduce or ease the stress of traveling.

199

ARRIVAL AT THE SHOW

UNLOADING AND PENNING
It is important for the welfare of your sheep to get them unloaded as soon as you arrive at the show or fairgrounds. Get them unloaded and into their pens before doing anything else.

If there isn't any bedding down in their pens, unload them into the pens anyway. Put down bedding as soon as possible so the sheep stay clean.

The sooner your sheep are settled in their new surroundings, the better off they will be.

FEED AND WATER
Once the sheep are in their pens, they should be given fresh water to which buffered electrolytes have been added. Don't let the sheep's first drink be more than a pint of water. More than a pint may cause scouring.

Don't give your sheep feed at this time. Give them a little hay if they traveled to the show on an empty stomach. This will help carry them over until their normal feeding time.

It is important to duplicate and follow the same feeding schedule that the sheep were on at home. Don't make any changes while at the show. This can throw sheep off feed and cause them to stop eating or to scour.

PROVIDING AIR MOVEMENT

Many shows and fairs are held during hot weather. Most sheep barns have poor air circulation. Hang a box fan up and direct the air onto your sheep to keep them cool and provide for air circulation.

Heatstress -- Sheep who become overheated pant like a dog with their mouth open. This is one sign of heatstress. Some other signs are trembling in the rear legs, arched back, standing with all four legs gathered under the body, and often an above normal temperature. If a sheep appears sick and has some of these signs, contact a veterinarian or refer to a good sheep care book for methods of treatment.

REDUCING STRESS

After the initial chores have been taken care of, leave your sheep alone and let them rest. Check on them several times for signs of stress or heatstress but don't handle them for the rest of the day unless they are not acting normal.

By allowing the sheep a rest period and by not handling them, you will avoid much of the stress associated some times with traveling or unfamiliar surroundings. Final preparations for the show should wait until the day after traveling.

CARE OF SHEEP AT THE SHOW

Try to keep the same schedule for your sheep while at the show that you had while at home. This includes feeding the same amount of feed and hay; providing fresh, clean water several times a day; and walking exercise. Exercising your sheep while at the shows helps keep them healthy.

Most shows have a veterinarian on the grounds. Ask the veterinarian to look at your sheep if they appear sick.

The most common illnesses seen in show sheep are those that begin as a result of stress.

Show sheep can become stressed from washing; trimming; poor ventilation and crowding on trailers while traveling; changes in feeding times or amounts; crowded pens while at the show; dust; and temperature variations. Good management of these situations will help to keep health problems low.

STRESS-REDUCING SHOW PRACTICES

There are several things that you can do to prevent most stress-caused illnesses. Cut down on as many forms of stress as you can by doing the following:

(1) -- Don't overcrowd sheep in pens. Get enough pens for the number of animals that you have to avoid this.

(2) -- Feed sheep on time and feed them the same amount as at home. Provide them with fresh, clean water. Each sheep should get a minimum of 1 quart of water per day. Offer them water with added buffered electrolytes.

(3) -- Make sure your sheep don't eat too much straw if straw is used as bedding in the pens. Straw can fill the rumen and the sheep may not eat their grain. This can cause digestive tract upsets such as indigestion and constipation.

Feed your sheep a little hay while at the show even if they have not been getting hay at home. This reduces the amount of straw sheep are inclined to eat.

(4) -- Each day that you work on your sheep, and on the morning of the show, give them an injection of Vitamin B Complex to help reduce the effects of stress.

(5) -- Exercise and work on sheep early in the morning or in the evening after the temperature is cooler.

(6) -- Check your sheep each day for signs of stress or illness. Some of the first signs are droopy ears or not eating. Show sheep usually have a good, healthy appetite.

If one of the animals is reluctant to eat or stops eating before the others it may mean the animal is becoming ill. Check with the veterinarian or treat the animal as soon as you see other signs indicating illness.

SHOW DAY

The day you have been looking forward to has finally arrived.

I can still remember how nervous I was the first time I exhibited sheep in a showring. Don't let those little butterflies in your stomach bother you too much. Once you get in the showring, you will relax and do just fine.

Take care of the last minute things you need to do for your sheep to get them ready for their class and then relax.

FEED AND WATER
On show day, if you show in the morning, you shouldn't give your sheep hay or water until after they

have been shown. This helps prevent a pot-belly appearance. Sheep who will not be shown until the afternoon should be given grain or feed pellets and a little water at their normal morning feeding.

ADVANCE PREPARATIONS FOR SHOWING
Study the showring in advance of the show. Sheep look best when their front legs are placed on slightly higher ground than are their rear legs.

If possible, look over the showring on the day of the show to see if there are any low spots in it that you may want to avoid while showing your sheep.

Try to watch some classes being shown before your class is called. Check to see how the judge lines up the class. Some place sheep from left to right while others place from right to left. Plan to arrive in the showring early enough that you can line up at the top of the class.

PRESHOW TOUCH-UP
Allow enough time before entering the showring to make sure your sheep are ready to be shown.

(1) -- Use a clean damp wash cloth and wipe the face and ears of your sheep. Make sure the insides of the ears are clean.

(2) -- To bring out the natural dark luster of the hair on black face sheep, take a dry cloth and rub over the hair of the face and legs several times to bring out the natural oils in the hair.

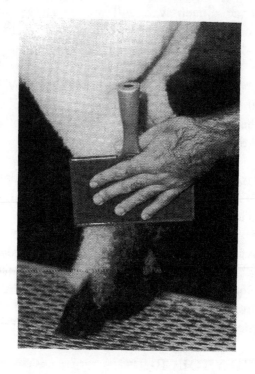

(3) -- If there are any marks or indentations in the fleece after the blanket has been removed, take your pocket card and gently fix these areas.

(4) -- Make sure there is no straw, wood shavings, or dirt anywhere on the body. Especially check the belly.

SHOWING

If you don't know when you are to show, find out or stay close enough to the ring so that you can hear the announcer when your class is called. It's important to be on time for your class.

Once you enter the showring, look for the judge. Judges often watch exhibitors as they enter the showring. Always be polite and mannerly to everyone and always handle your sheep in a gentle manner. This is often the judge's first impression of you. Make sure it is a good one.

After you spot the judge, move your animal smoothly into position in the line-up. Don't crowd anyone already in line. Try to leave 2 to 3 feet between your sheep and other sheep in the line-up.

Set up your sheep's legs as soon as you are in line and then squat down and try to be as unnoticeable as possible. From this position, you will also be able to keep your animal's back level.

Almost everyone who has shown sheep was a little nervous the first time they entered the showring. Try to relax and remain calm because nervousness can be picked up by the animal you are showing. This may result in a more difficult animal to handle and show.

After entering the ring, be alert and follow the directions given to you by the judge or ringman. Don't worry that you will forget something. Once you are in that showring everything you have practiced will come back to you naturally.

The judge will most likely move you around and place you in a different position in the line-up than the one where you originally started. As soon as this happens, set-up your sheep. Then move to a position between your animal and the sheep that is placed before you. This allows the judge to compare more easily your sheep to the other sheep in the class.

The judge may reconsider his placement and move your animal up a place or two.

Always try to make your animal appear alert and attentive when the judge comes before you for a front view of your sheep.

To get the animal's attention and cause it to bring its ears forward in an alert position, pick up a small handful of dirt or wood shavings from the showring and drop it out in front of the animal.

Your sheep may try to back up a little when the judge comes up in front of it. To prevent the animal from doing this, put your hand under its dock. Be prepared to put pressure on the dock if the animal starts to back up.

If you make a mistake, don't let it bother you. Everyone including the judge has made mistakes at some time while exhibiting sheep. Just do the best you can and remember that showing sheep is supposed to be a learning experience and most of all fun.

AFTER SHOWING

It is important to conduct yourself in the same manner while exiting the showring that you did when you entered the showring.

The show isn't over until you return your animal to its pen. Put the blanket and hood back on the sheep unless you will be showing that animal in another class or showing for champion.

After you are through showing, make sure your sheep have been given hay and water before you leave the pen. Remove any blankets, hoods, and halters so that the animal doesn't chew on or get entangled in them. Safely fasten the pen.

You are now free to celebrate the effort you made at showing your animal.

If you didn't win your class or do as well as you would have liked, don't give up and become discouraged. Everyone who makes an effort to select, feed, care for, fit and show sheep are winners just because they tried.

Remember that there will always be other shows. If you keep at it, and gain more experience, you will become a class winner!

INDEX

212

215

217

Pepto Bismol, 159
Pneumonia
    sign of, 35
Pneumonia prevention, 157
Pneumonia vaccine, 75
Poodle clip, 86
Pot-belly, 46, 92
Preshow touch-up, 205
Preventive medicine, 72, 73
Private treaty, 56

Rear legs
    muscling, 48
Rear stance, 48
    leg width, 48
Ringworm
    antibiotic cleanser, 162
    antibiotic shampoo, 161
Rough blocking, 171

Safe space, 64
Safety, 72
Salt mix, vitamin-mineral, 97
Selection
    conformation, 38
    Signs of good health, 34
    Signs of ill health, 35
    signs of ill health, 35
    type, 36
Self-feeding, 104
Sex of lamb, 52
Shearing
    before show, 183
    belly, 85
    breeches, 82
    directions for belly, 169
    equipment suppliers, 79
    fleece length, 82
    heatstress prevention, 79

219

221

SUPPLIERS

CEE-DER Sheep Products
Box 2404
Canmore
Alberta, Canada, T0L 0M0
(403) 678-2220, 6785251

KV Vet Supply Co.
Rt. 1, South Hwy 15 & 92, P.O. Box 245
David City, NE 68632
1-800 423-8211

Premier Sheep Supplies
Box 89
Washington, IA 52353
1-800-282-6631

Pipestone Veterinary Supply
1300 S. Hwy 75, P.O. Box 188
Pipestone, MN 56164
1-800-658-2523

S. B. Wallace & Company
P.O. Box 87
Marlinton, WV   24954
1-800-233-6914

Sheepman Supply
5449 Gov. Barbour St., P.O. Box 100
Barboursville, VA 22923
1-800-336-3005

Sheep Care Books
by Laura Lawson

MANAGING YOUR EWE & HER NEWBORN LAMBS - Detect, Diagnose, Treat 120 ewe & newborn problems from infertility in ewes to weaning stress in lambs. Use the author's unique system of Diagnostic Check Sheets, Symptom Flow Charts, and Treatment to solve problems.

Breeding thru weaning management of ewe & lambs is also covered. 382 pages full size 8x11, 87 illustrations ---**$29.95**

LAMB PROBLEMS - Detect, Diagnose, and Treat 152 problems. Respiratory, scours, feet, prolaps, and digestive are just some of the problems covered. Uses the same unique system discribed above. Fully illustrated.-----**$29.95**

SHOWING SHEEP - Covers selecting, feeding, fitting, & showing sheep. Written for 4-H, FFA & Adults. An excellent reference for both the beginner or the experienced wanting to learn more about the care and showing of sheep.

This 224 page book has twice the information as any book on showing and none are priced lower . ---------------**$12.95**

Hoof Care - Trimming, walk-through footbath, prevent and treat foot rot, injection treatments. 36 pages with plans and illustrations. ---**$3.95**

Home Remedies for diarrhea, pain, bloat, etc. using common household items. Includes colostrum formulas. -----------**$3.95**

Chilled & Weak Lambs - Revive with warming boxes, enema & dextrose therapy. Includes Symptom, Treatment & Cause sections on chilled lambs.-------------------------**$3.95**

LDF Publications   **Call toll free 1-800-258-6992**